National Curriculum
Key Stage 3 Age 13–14

National Test Practice Papers

Practice English
Practice Maths
Practice Science

3 in 1 Contents

Practice Papers

Key Stage 3
National Tests

ENGLISH

How the Key Stage 3 National Tests will affect your education

- All students in Year 9 (age 13–14) will take National Tests in English, Mathematics and Science. These important tests are held in May each year and are designed to be an objective assessment of the work you will have done during Key Stage 3 (Years 7–9) of the National Curriculum.

- You will also have your school work assessed by your teachers. These teacher assessments will be set alongside your results in the National Tests to give a clear picture of your overall achievement.

- In July, the test results together with the teacher assessments will be reported to parents/guardians.

- The results may be used by your teacher to help place you in the appropriate teaching group for some GCSE courses next year.

How this book will help your education

- This book offers plenty of practice in the type of questions you will face in the Key Stage 3 National Test for English.

- The answers and a mark scheme have been provided to allow you to check how you have done.

- A unique marking grid allows you to record your results and estimate the level of the National Curriculum at which you are working.

KS3 English Contents

What you need to know about the National Tests

What is the purpose of National Tests?

The tests, taken by students in Year 9, have several functions:

- they provide the government with a snapshot picture of attainment throughout the country, enabling it to make judgements about whether standards are improving nationally;
- they give information to OFSTED about schools' achievements, so that they can judge which schools are improving and which are deemed to be failing their students;
- they give you information about your progress compared with national standards;
- they may be used by teachers to place you in the appropriate teaching group for the GCSE courses starting in Year 10.

How do the tests work?

In May of Year 9, you will take tests on the core subjects of English, Mathematics and Science. In English there are three tests. The tests are not marked in school by a teacher, but posted off to an external marker, who is often a teacher in another school or a retired teacher. External markers have been trained in marking the tests so that all students' test papers throughout the country are marked to the same standard.

Once the tests have been marked, the mark is translated into a 'level'. The level that each mark corresponds to is decided according to results gained in pre-tests and the tests themselves. It varies slightly from year to year. The test papers, marks and levels are returned to your school in July. The levels are then reported to your parents/guardians.

What do the tests assess?

The tests are designed to assess your knowledge, skills and understanding in the context of the programme of study set out in the National Curriculum. This can be found on the National Curriculum website, www.nc.uk.net.

The programme of study is divided into three sections, called Attainment Targets:

- En1 – Speaking and listening.
- En2 – Reading.
- En3 – Writing.

En1 is assessed by your teacher. En2 and En3 are assessed by written tests.

What are the levels and what do they mean?

There is a set of benchmark standards that measure a student's progress through the first three Key Stages of the National Curriculum. Attainment is measured in steps called 'levels', from 1 to 7. The National Curriculum document sets out the knowledge, skills and understanding that students should demonstrate at each level. The government target is for students to achieve level 2 at the end of Key Stage 1, level 4 at the end of Key Stage 2 and level 5 or 6 at the end of Key Stage 3. The chart below shows these government targets.

How should I progress?

At the end of Key Stage 3, students take tests targeted at level 4 to level 7. Students who achieve an exceptionally high mark, well above that needed for the top level, are assessed as Gifted and Talented.

How does this book help me?

This book gives you practice in answering the type of question that you will face in the actual tests. By practising questions in this way, you will feel under less pressure and be more relaxed. Being relaxed helps students to perform at their best in tests. We have targeted the questions at levels 4–7, allowing you to become familiar with the types of question that are asked in the tests.

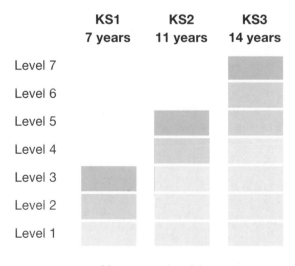

Exceeded targets for age group

Achieved targets for age group

Working towards targets for age group

How you should progress

Preparing and practising for the English Test

These practice papers are modelled on the 'real thing'. Working through the book will help you to become more familiar with the format of the tests.

What are the key features of this book?

This book contains all you need to prepare for the tests:

- National Curriculum requirements – key information for each of Attainment Targets En2 (Reading) and En3 (Writing).
- Questions – three practice test papers targeted at levels 4–7.
- Answers – showing the responses that will gain credit in the tests and how the marks are allocated.
- Level charts – what the marks mean in terms of National Curriculum levels.

How should I use this book?

Familiarity helps to take away some of the fear of the tests. If you know what to expect, you will feel more comfortable!

- Make sure you have plenty of rest – and time for fun – in the run up to the tests.
- Choose a warm, comfortable place to revise and to try the practice tests. Working in timed conditions will help you to pace your work in the actual tests.

- You will need plenty of lined paper to complete answers to the practice papers.
- Learn from your mistakes. Perhaps look at one or two particular issues to try to improve before your next revision session.
- If you have any concerns or there is something you are having problems with, consult your teacher for help – that's what they are there for!

Important notes

Make sure that you do not use this book to add to the pressure you are already under.

Think positive at all times! It is easy to get stressed when doing your homework and revision. Try to stay calm; if you feel stressed, have a snack break or take a walk.

Look at questions together with friends, talking about ways to answer them. Use the examiner's suggestions in the answer section of this book to help.

When you mark your work, remember to highlight and congratulate yourself on good answers and ideas. Do not get trapped into noticing just your mistakes!

What does the level mean?

The tests in this book give a guide as to the level that you are likely to achieve in the actual tests. We hope that, through practice, these tests will give you the confidence to achieve your best. By working through the answers and notes, you should be able to improve your achievement.

So that you can compare your achievement with national standards, the chart below shows the percentage of students awarded each level in a typical year.

How do I prepare to take the actual tests?

A few days before the test:

- work through the questions in Papers 1, 2 and 3 again and make sure that you understand the correct answers to each question;

- check that you know what test papers you will be taking and when these are to be sat;

- double check that you have the necessary equipment.

Finally, remember that if you have prepared thoroughly for the tests, you can be confident that you will do your best.

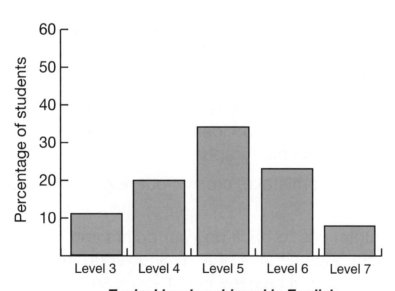

Typical levels achieved in English

Top tips for tests – on the day

- Read through papers before you begin to make sure you understand **exactly** what is required. Note, or highlight, important points such as number of questions to be answered and time allowed. Don't be caught out!

- Keep an eye on the time – don't spend so long on a question that you run out of time for the others.

- Read questions very carefully. It is too easy to see key words such as 'Lady Macbeth' and to just write down everything you know about her rather than answering the actual question. It may be a good idea to underline key words such as 'compare' in a question to help you to focus.

- Use the help given on the paper. When examiners give you points to consider, these are prompts to help you.

- Make notes on the paper before you start. Don't write in full sentences – it's a waste of time. Just note down odd words and phrases to help you get your ideas organised.

- Check out how many marks each question is 'worth' – this will be next to the question. This helps you to decide exactly how much detail the examiner expects. Spend a bit more time on questions with more marks – but don't neglect the others. Marks soon add up!

- Write answers in full sentences. You should also write in paragraphs. It's a good idea to leave a space – perhaps a line – between each paragraph to make your work easier to read.

- If you make a mistake, cross it out neatly and change your answer.

- Use quotations to back up your points and ideas, but don't copy out huge chunks of text. Shorter quotations that focus on your idea will give the effect you want.

- For maximum marks, check your spelling, grammar and punctuation.

- If you get stuck on a question, move on and come back to it later. It may seem much clearer once you stop panicking!

- If you have any time left, read your answers back to yourself to make sure they make sense and that you have not missed anything. Check your spelling again, too.

Instructions

The Key Stage 3 National Test includes three papers.

Paper 1

Reading Paper

This paper assesses how you have understood the three texts you read (these can be found in the English Booklet). The paper allows for 15 minutes' reading and one hour for the test itself.

Paper 2

Writing Paper

This paper is a long Writing Task. It will be timetabled to be taken during the same test session as the Reading Paper, but you will be given a break between them on the day of your test. Make sure you take this break when you are practising! The Writing Paper takes 45 minutes.

Paper 3

You can also think of Paper 3 as the Shakespeare Paper.

Section A: Writing Task

This short Writing Task will be related to ideas or themes arising from the study of the Shakespeare play. This task should last about 30 minutes.

Section B: Reading Task

This part of the paper tests your reading and understanding of Shakespeare, and will be based on the detailed study of two sections from one of three Shakespeare plays. This task should last about 45 minutes.

Reading Tasks

To practise for the Reading Tasks, you will need to use the separate reading booklet, found at the back of this book. This contains three texts for the Reading Paper 1 and two Shakespeare extracts for the Reading Task in Paper 3.

How to approach the papers

Try to answer all the questions.

Read the questions carefully.

If you think, after reading a question carefully, that you cannot answer it, leave it and come back to it later.

Write your answers fully on lined paper.

Look at the number of marks for each part of a question. This is shown in a box in the margin, for example:

If a question is worth one mark, often a single point is needed. A question worth two marks would need two distinct points to be made. You are very unlikely to score two marks with a single word answer.

There is also a box showing the maximum number of marks for each section. You can write in your subtotal, so that you can see at a glance how you are doing.

Read your answers carefully to yourself and make sure you have clearly expressed what you mean.

GOOD LUCK!

INSTRUCTIONS

Carefully detach pages 1–14 of the English Booklet at the back of this book. Fasten the pages together to make your own English Booklet. You will need to read pages 2–9 for Paper 1.

This Reading Paper is divided into three parts: *Fairtrade Fortnight 2002* (an informative article about The Fairtrade Foundation), *A Sheep Fair* (a poem by Thomas Hardy) and *Saturday in Sydney Market* (recollections about the writer's [Lynn Huggins-Cooper's] childhood).

You have an hour to complete the Reading Paper, with an additional 15 minutes of reading time. Use it wisely! Bear the following things in mind as you read – they will give you a clue about what the examiner is looking for:

- Where the question says 'find and copy' or 'select and copy', it means exactly that – copy down the exact words you have read. Do not paraphrase or put the passage into your own words.

- When a question asks 'why?', think about the reasons for the writer's choice of words – don't just describe what he or she has said.

- The boxes in the margins will show you how many marks are allocated for each question. Remember that questions that have a higher number of marks need detailed answers. Use quotes from the writing to back up your point of view.

The Reading Paper carries 50 marks.

Gifted and Talented Tip!

To score highly on this paper you need to make sure that you answer **all** parts of **all** questions. Read the questions and break them down into parts if necessary. In your answer you are then more likely to show that you have given a full answer.

Inconsistent answers are not likely to get the highest marks – plan and check.

Paper 1: Reading Paper
Levels 4–7

START
FINISH

Fairtrade Fortnight 2002

2
Q1

1   Asda buys fair trade items to support producers in developing countries. Make a list of the products mentioned in the article.

....

....

....

1
Q2a

2   Explain why the inverted commas are used in the paragraphs below.

---

a   He began by weeding, hoeing, pruning and harvesting, then in 1999 he was promoted to the Field Monitoring and Assessment Team. "I am proud of my job. The managers are good to us, and if we are sick the company takes good care of us."

....

....

1
Q2b

---

b   From 4 to 17 March there will be Fairtrade posters and booklets in store and you can "Share the Passion" in the quality of the produce and the fair trade that it promotes.

....

....

3 Why was the Fairtrade Foundation set up?

....

....

....

4 a Match the paragraph heading to the idea that the paragraph contains.

1 Sunny outlook

a How to get involved in Fairtrade activities to help even more than the 500,000 producers already involved.

2 Making a difference

b Payments are made for social and economic developments such as education and health.

3 How it all works

c An explanation of how Fairtrade helps workers help themselves.

b In the paragraph headed "A price that's right", the writer explains how the farmers are given a fair price for their produce. Select and copy **two** phrases that emphasise this idea.

....

....

....

Max. 9
Qs 1–4
subtotal

13

2
Q5

5 Complete the following list with details from the text about the work of The Fairtrade Foundation.

Date of Fairtrade Fortnight 2002: ....

Fairtrade website address: ....

Name and price of Fairtrade chocolate: ....

....

Number of producers helped so far: ....

Names of three celebrity sponsors: ....

....

6
Q6

6 The text aims to persuade the reader to buy fair trade products. How successful is the article?

You should write about:

- how the language is used to convey the idea that fair trade is important because it changes people's lives

- the layout of the text – including photographs, headings and coloured panels.

....

....

....

....

....

....

....

....

....

....

A Sheep Fair

7 Find and copy **two** similes in Hardy's poem *A Sheep Fair*. How do the similes add to the visual image of the fair created in the reader's mind?

2
Q7

....

....

....

....

....

8 Why do you think Hardy used the word 'bedrenched' instead of 'wet' in the line '*And wipes his book, bedrenched and smeared* …'?

1
Q8

....

....

2
Q9

9 What effect is created by the rhythm of these lines, which describe the sheep? *'Jammed tight, to turn, or lie, or lunge, They strive in vain.'*

....

....

....

....

....

....

2
Q10

10 Select and copy a phrase that creates a 'wet' sound to describe the rain by the use of alliteration.
Why does the phrase make the reader think of rain?

....

....

....

....

....

....

11 a What impression do you get of the way Hardy feels about animal markets from this poem? Refer to the words used to support your ideas.

3
Q11a

....

....

....

....

....

....

....

b How do you think Hardy sees the people at the auction? If he feels sympathetic towards the sheep, does he feel animosity for the humans?

2
Q11b

....

....

....

....

....

....

Max. 9
Qs
9–11
subtotal

12 Hardy describes the shepherds, saying they 'reek against the rails'. According to the *Westminster English Dictionary*, 'reek' means 'to emit vapour, usually that which is warm and moist; to steam; to smoke'.

What picture do you think Hardy was trying to create in the mind of the reader?

Max. 14
Qs
7–12
subtotal

....

....

....

....

....

....

....

Saturday in Sydney Street

13 Find and copy **two** pieces of information that suggest that Lynn's family were regular visitors to the Sydney Street Market. Explain why you have chosen each piece of evidence.

For example:

Evidence: 'On a Saturday morning, the ritual was always the same.'

Explanation: The word 'ritual' means something that happens in a certain way, regularly. The sentence says that every Saturday morning, the same thing happened – in this case, getting in the car to go to the market.

Evidence: ....

....

Explanation: ....

....

....

Evidence: ....

....

Explanation: ....

....

....

14 Do you think the writer has happy memories of her childhood? You should write about the things she remembers and the words she uses to describe them.

5
Q14

....

....

....

....

....

....

Max. 9
Qs
13–14
subtotal

4
Q15

15 Find and copy **two** pieces of information that suggest that the writer does not hold the view that young people are interested in very different things today than they were in the past. Explain why you have chosen each piece of evidence.

For example:

Evidence: 'when my own children settle down to read books about Buffy, Angel and the X Files I reckon little has changed.'

Explanation: The writer is talking about books that have the same sort of themes as the comics she used to enjoy as a child. 'Buffy' and 'Angel' are about vampires and demons, and 'X Files' is about aliens and strange unexplained happenings.

Evidence: ....

....

....

Explanation: ....

....

....

Evidence: ....

....

Explanation: ....

....

16 How do we know that the writer thought American things were exciting and glamorous?

6
Q16

- Think about how she compares English things with their American counterparts.

- Refer to examples of American things she had seen and wanted to own.

....

....

....

....

....

....

....

....

....

....

....

Max. 19
Qs
13–16
subtotal

....

INSTRUCTIONS

The Writing Paper requires a detailed answer. Do not just think that if you write more, you will get more marks. The examiners are looking for work that is interesting and suits the purpose of the task set. For example, if you are asked to do a persuasive piece, you should include a range of persuasive techniques, like making someone feel guilty, speaking directly to them, and so on. If you are writing descriptively, use adjectives, adverbs, similes, metaphors, your senses and your feelings, and so on.

There are lots of other different types of writing that you could be tested on here, for example, argumentative, instructional, informative and so on – they are all the types that you will have covered in Years 7 to 9. Your revision should include looking back at the different forms of writing that you have covered and remembering the features of each type of writing.

On this particular task, your writing will be marked out of 25 for the following:

A Sentence structure and punctuation (5 marks)

B Text structure and organisation (use of paragraphs and your overall plan) (5 marks)

C Composition and effect (how well your writing fits the task and suits its audience) (15 marks)

You should spend around 45 minutes on this section.

Paper 2: Writing Paper
Levels 4–7

Gifted and Talented Tip!

To get the highest marks you should try and show some originality. For example, if you are doing a descriptive piece of writing avoid using worn-out similes and adjectives. Saying that something is 'as cold as ice' shows that you can use similes, but lots of other people have used that same idea before. Better writers do things like creating unusual figures of speech (similes, metaphors, and so on) and they use vocabulary that is carefully chosen. If you're using everyday vocabulary throughout your writing, then you aren't showing the marker that you are a good writer!

| START | |
| FINISH | |

Imagine that the council has made an announcement that your local street market, where you have always shopped, is to be demolished to make way for an executive housing development. You are going to write a letter to the council, protesting at this decision and trying to persuade it not to go ahead.

Make sure you use plenty of interesting and vivid language, but remember that this is a formal letter.

Write your letter on a separate sheet of paper.

PLANNING SHEET

Before you start your writing, make some brief notes to help organise your ideas.

Why is the market important to local people? For example, how far is it to the nearest supermarket, cheap food, historic reasons for preservation, etc.

Why is the market important to you personally? Include descriptions of the market.

Remember to include a strong conclusion to your letter.

You do not need to include an address at the top of your letter. Start 'Dear Sir/Madam'.

Paper 3

This paper consists of Section A (a Shorter Writing Task) and Section B (a Reading Task).

There is only one way to prepare for the Shakespeare Paper – read the play!

It is also worth getting hold of a guide to the play that is appropriate for Key Stage 3. Guides, which are readily available, can help you to understand the old-fashioned language and themes of Shakespeare's plays. They should be read **as well as** the whole play – not **instead** of it!

Watch videos of the films to help you to understand the plays and go to see any productions at the theatre. The more you know about the background of the story of the play, the easier it will be to answer the questions.

Remember, do not just try to write everything you know about the play – actually read the question carefully and circle key words such as 'compare'. Make sure that you answer the question that has been set!

Do not just copy out huge chunks of text – that will not earn you marks! Use short, focused quotations to back up your ideas. Pick out words and phrases and explain them.

Remember to pace yourself – you do not have long to answer the questions! The examiner will be looking for proof that you understand the play. The questions may look at the plot, ideas, behaviour and motivation of characters, the staging of scenes and the language of the play.

Remember, though, that you will need to write clearly and that you should check the organisation, spelling and punctuation of your answers. Make sure that your handwriting is tidy and well formed, so that the examiner can read your work.

INSTRUCTIONS

You have 30 minutes for this task. Read the question carefully and use the planning sheet provided on page 28. Remember to use interesting vocabulary, and read your work back to yourself to ensure it makes sense, and says what you want it to say!

As in Paper 2, you could be asked to write in any one of a variety of styles. The advice there about revising how to use the features of different types of writing that you have learnt at Key Stage 3 applies equally here.

The difference between this writing task and Paper 2 is that the marker is looking for slightly different aspects of your writing.

This writing task carries 25 marks, awarded for:

D Sentence structure/punctuation and text organisation – 10 marks (not assessed in Paper 2)

E Composition and effect – 10 marks

F Spelling – 5 marks (not assessed in Paper 2)

Gifted and Talented Tip!

This is a shorter task – again try to show some originality in your choice of words, but also try to vary the types of sentence that you write. Sentence structure and text organisation are worth 10 of the marks!

The marker will be looking for a good writer to show that they can use sentences in a variety of ways.

For example, use sentences of different lengths to achieve certain effects. Short ones might be used to emphasise a key point. Longer sentences might be used to build up tension.

Use sentence types such as rhetorical questions, statements and commands if they are appropriate to the task.

If you can use a variety of sentence types appropriately to create effects and to strengthen your writing, you will be able to achieve higher marks.

START

FINISH

In *Macbeth*, Shakespeare creates a frightening mood whenever the witches appear. Think of a place and time where you were scared as a small child. Write a brief description of the place and how you felt.

You should write only three paragraphs to:

- inform the reader of why you were scared.

- describe the place as vividly as you can – use:

  sights   sounds   smells   tastes   touch.

- explain how you felt.

Write your description on a separate piece of paper.

PLANNING SHEET

Before you start writing, make some brief notes about the place. Remember to organise your work into three paragraphs.

Reasons for choosing that place:

Description of the place:

Why was the place so memorable? Why were you scared?
How did you feel?

Paper 3: Section B:
Levels 4–7   Reading Task

INSTRUCTIONS

In the actual test you will answer **one** question in this section. Two have been provided in this book to enable you to practise. Choose **either** the question about *Macbeth* **or** the question about *Twelfth Night*. You can always look at the other question later.

You have 45 minutes for this test. The scenes to be read can be found in the English Booklet at the back of this book.

The Shakespeare Reading Task carries 18 marks.

Gifted and Talented Tip!

Do not ramble and give extra information just because you know it – only answer the parts of the question set.

Organise your work sensibly. Plan your answer! Spend 5 to 10 minutes planning and 35 to 40 minutes writing.

Give a sense of how you feel about the ideas in the questions. Use phrases like 'The words "(insert quotation)" make me feel/suggest to me/imply to me' and so on. This will show the marker that you are not just trotting out the ideas your teachers have spoken to you about.

START

FINISH

Macbeth: Act 1 Scene 3 and Act 3 Scene 1

In these extracts we see how Macbeth starts to realise that he can become King instead of Duncan.

What do we learn about Macbeth's desire to become king from these extracts?

Support your ideas by referring to the extracts from the play.

....

....

....

....

....

....

....

....

....

....

....

....

....

....

....

....

START	
FINISH	

Twelfth Night Act 2 Scene 3 and Act 4 Scene 2

In these extracts there is a lot of joking, fooling and deception from the characters involved.

What does the language and behaviour of the characters tell us about the themes and ideas of the play?

Support your ideas by referring to the extracts from the play.

....

....

....

....

....

....

....

....

....

....

....

....

....

....

....

....

....

....

....

....

....

....

....

....

Answers

Write your marks into the Marking grid on page 55.

Fairtrade Fortnight 2002

1 Fairtrade bananas, Percol Coffee (Latin American and Columbia), Day Chocolate Divine milk chocolate, Cafédirect coffee

2 marks for complete list

2 **a** shows speech

   b is a quotation from the Fairtrade Fortnight campaign

1 mark for each correct answer; 2 marks

3 The Fairtrade foundation was set up to ensure that food and drink producers in developing nations get a better deal, and that all products carrying the Fairtrade mark meet international standards of fair trade.

1 mark for any quote from the appropriate section of the text

4 **a**

   1 Sunny outlook — **b**

   2 Making a difference — **a**

   3 How it all works —————→ **c**

   a How to get involved in Fairtrade activities to help even more than the 500,000 producers already involved.

   b Payments are made for social and economic developments such as education and health.

   c An explanation of how Fairtrade helps workers help themselves.

1 mark for 2 correct answers; 2 marks for 3 correct answers

   b "Fairtrade products are bought directly from farmers at a guaranteed price", "farmers get a greater share", "the price covers the cost of production and ensures growers get a decent wage".

Any two for 2 marks

5

Date of Fairtrade Fortnight 2002:	4–17 March
Fairtrade website address:	www.fairtrade.org.uk
Name and price of Fairtrade chocolate:	Day Chocolate Divine £1.40 for 150g
Number of producers helped so far:	500,000
Names of three celebrity sponsors:	Any three from: Tony Blair, George Alagiah, Sanjeev Bhaskar, Honor Blackman, Cherie Booth QC, Angus Deayton, Judi Dench, Dawn French, Joanna Lumley, Paul Merton, Nicholas Parsons, Gary Rhodes, Griff Rhys Jones and Victoria Wood.

2 marks for completely correct answer

6 The focus of this question is to identify and comment on the writer's purposes and viewpoints and the effect of the text on you, the reader. Features of the text that you might include are:

- Individual words, e.g. proud, decent, safety, fair.
- Phrases such as economic development, trade unions, no child or forced labour, regular wages, environmental improvements.
- Some mention of introduction/increase in health care and education, avoidance of debt and long-term trading relationships.
- Elements of its layout, e.g. the use of bright, interesting photos to support the text, the use of panels or boxes in colour to lead the eye and the use of larger, coloured subheadings to break up the text and make it interesting.

Award 1 mark for answers that give some response to the question, possibly repeating words from the prompts in the question, or copying from the text without comment.

Award 2–4 marks for answers that refer back to several specific details in the text in addition to your own comment or judgement. To gain 4 marks you should make reference to both prompts.

Award 5–6 marks for answers that include a wide range of specific details from the text including reference to the language the writer used. In order to be awarded 6 points, you should have included a clear, supported judgement about the success of the text with reference to both prompts.

A Sheep Fair

7 Two from:

Simile: 'buyers' hat-brims fill like pails'

Imagery: the hat-brims fill up like buckets; a strong picture of something filling with water – emphasises how much rain has fallen

Simile: Any quote from the appropriate section of the text 'horns are soft as finger-nails'

Imagery: the horns are pliable like fingernails; makes the reader think of touching the horns and how they would feel

Simile: 'wool of the ewes is like a sponge'

Imagery: the wool is soft and soaks up the rainwater. Makes the reader think of how very wet the sheep are; also the idea that the fleece is soft and squeezable like a sponge

2 marks if two similes and a description are given;
1 mark for one simile and a description; or
1 mark for two similes without descriptions

8   'Bedrenched' is a more descriptive word than 'wet'. It suggests that something has happened to the book – it is a more active description of what has happened. 'Bedrenched' is quite onomatopoeic – it sounds heavy and laden down by water. This helps to create a 'sodden' picture in the reader's mind.

1 mark for a pertinent description of how the word adds to the atmosphere of the poem

9   The words 'Jammed tight, to turn, or lie, or lunge' have a short, stabbing rhythm, which suggests the short, ineffectual attempts of the sheep to move about.

'They strive in vain' has a smoother rhythm, which adds a sense of hopelessness to the sheep's attempts to move.

2 marks

10   The repetition of the 's' sound in 'spill small cascades when they shift their stand' creates a sibilant, wet sound that makes the reader think of heavy rain.

2 marks

11 a   Possibly he feels a little saddened; his use of the drenching rain could be to create a downcast mood. The lines:

'Jammed tight, to turn, or lie, or lunge,
They strive in vain.'

suggest that he feels some sympathy for the sheep who are powerless and cannot do anything to make themselves comfortable.

The description of the dogs as soaking wet, with 'tucked-in tails' suggests that even the dogs are miserable.

3 marks for any pertinent ideas
supported by quotations from the text

b   Hardy does not seem to feel any animosity towards the humans in the poem; he seems sympathetic.

When he describes the auctioneer, saying he 'rakes the rain from his face with the edge of his hand,' we feel sorry for the man who is soaking and probably tired.

He also seems to feel sorry for the men standing around in the rain, as he says:

'when they shift their stand
In the daylong rain.'

Again, he seems to feel sorry for them because they are tired and wet.

2 marks for any pertinent ideas
supported by quotations from the text

12 Possibly Hardy is trying to create a picture of the shepherds, gently steaming as they dry out in the warmth given out by the crush of bodies as they press together against the rails. He could also be referring to them smoking as they stand there.

2 marks

Saturday in Sydney Street

13 **Evidence**: 'the market pilgrimage was the highlight of my week'

Explanation: The word 'pilgrimage' suggests a special journey and the fact that the journey was the 'highlight of my week' suggests it happened on a weekly basis.

Evidence: 'I agonised every week – peanut brittle was a particular temptation – I always ended up clutching the same choice'

Explanation: The writer says she had a hard time deciding which sweets to buy 'every week' – suggesting a regular visit – and then she says she 'always ended up' with the same sweets, which also suggests that the visit to the sweetshop was regular.

1 mark for each point and one mark for each linked explanation
up to a total of 4 marks

14 'the warm rumble of our Dad's voice': The word 'warm' suggests love – a happy memory.

'always lit with bright sunshine': in memory, the sun was always shining – a happy time.

'we were happy to bypass these pleasures': there were so many pleasures to be had, some could be bypassed.

'even the food stalls were exciting': even the food stalls, something mundane and ordinary, were interesting.

'delight to be had'/'glutted pleasure' the seasonal nature of food remembered with pleasure.

'all manner of glorious sweets': the memory of fabulous, unusual sweets.

'my mouth's memory gushes at the thought': such a tasty memory that it makes the writer's mouth water.

'Bliss! … nothing today comes close': such a wonderful memory of a taste that everything seems disappointing today.

'The best was yet to come': makes it sound as though things just got better and better.

'Their glossy covers called me like a siren': the comics are remembered as exciting and mesmerising.

'I gobbled them down with relish': such exciting stories that they were devoured.

Award 1 mark for answers that make simple, general or brief comments (especially for a comment that does little more than repeat the prompts).

Award 2 or 3 marks for answers that support a general comment with 2 or 3 details supporting the prompts given in the question.

Award 4 or 5 marks for answers that address each of the prompts, giving detailed answers which comment on the significance of the evidence given to prove the viewpoints.

15 **Evidence**: 'Kids had unhealthy tastes in junk food, even then!'
Explanation: Children past and present like 'junk food', such as chips.

Evidence: 'Like all children, past and present, I must have driven my Dad mad … my own children'
Explanation: The writer says that she made her dad wait as she made up her mind about which sweets she wanted; her own children love sweet stalls in the market today and make her wait.

Award 1 mark for each point and 1 mark for each linked explanation, up to a total of 4 marks

16 'These were no ordinary comics …These comics were imported from America. Their glossy covers called me like a siren.' The comics are compared to English comics such as '*Bunty*' and '*Whizzer and Chips*', which could not 'compete' despite their free gifts.

In the American comics, 'Even the advertisements were a source of fascination' – including advertisements for 'pet sea monkeys'. The writer says, 'I longed for them as I eyed my cat with ennui' – she was desperate to own the exotic pets rather than her own cat, which she looked at with boredom after seeing the advertisement.

She says, 'how wonderful to live in a country where you could have tiny marine monkeys as pets!' – she thought that America must be a fabulous place to live if you could have such exotic pets.

She longs to taste the American sweets and biscuits in the advertisements and compares them to 'boring' English food: 'what were Oreo cookies like? I was sure they would be delicious, compared to our boring old English fig rolls!'. She goes on to say that she was disappointed when she finally tasted an Oreo, as she had built it up in her mind as exciting and better than an English biscuit: 'the child inside me felt let down somehow. It was just another biscuit.'

Up to 6 marks, awarded for reference to appropriate evidence as given above.

For the full 6 marks, you need to make reference to comparisons between English and American comics, biscuits, etc.

Paper 2: Writing Paper Pages 22–24

The mark scheme given below is intended to help you decide what marks to award yourself for the Writing Paper. You should read through the descriptions for the bands in each section and decide on the 'best fit' – the description that most clearly describes your writing. You should then award yourself the marks appropriate to that description and write them in the Marking grid on page 55.

You will notice that each band in section C has three different marks available.

- If your writing satisfies half or more but not all of the criteria for a band, give yourself the lowest mark available for that band.
- If your writing fits all the criteria for a band (e.g. C3) but none of the criteria for the band above, give yourself the middle mark for your band (e.g. 8).
- If your writing satisfies all the criteria for a band (e.g. C3) and one of the criteria for the band above, give yourself the full marks for your band (e.g. 9).

It is important that you read through the sections in order, from A to C, so that you build up a picture of your writing – its strengths and weaknesses.

Section A: Sentence structure and punctuation

This section looks at how sentences and punctuation contribute to the meaning and effect of your writing.

Band A1

• Sentences and phrases are mostly linked with joining words like 'and', 'but' and 'when'. • Sentences are simple and may contain lots of repeated words and phrases. • Full stops, capital letters and exclamation marks are used to punctuate sentences, mostly accurately.

1 mark

Band A2

• Sentences are varied and more complex joining words like 'who' and 'which' are used. • Words like 'if' and 'because' are used to help give reasons and for emphasising ideas. • Commas are used quite accurately within sentences.

2 marks

Band A3

• Simple and more complex sentences are used – long sentences and short sentences are used successfully. • Suggestions are given, by using words like 'can' or 'would'. • A variety of punctuation is used with accuracy. • Different types of sentence, e.g. commands, questions or exclamations, are used in order to create more interesting effects.

3 marks

Band A4

• The writer begins sentences more skilfully, with words like 'usually', 'hopefully', etc. or by being impersonal, e.g. 'Some people believe that…'. • A range of punctuation is used and this is sometimes done for deliberate effect, e.g. brackets are used to put in asides and thoughts.

4 marks

Band A5

• Sentences are varied depending on the effect that the writer wishes to create.
• Simple sentences might be used, but to create effects, e.g. shock or surprise.
• Punctuation is used skilfully in order to make the reader speed up and slow down and to make the meaning of the writing perfectly clear.

5 marks

Section B: Text structure and organisation

This section focuses on how overall meaning and effect is put across through the way that the writing is organised and planned.

Band B1

• Ideas are mainly linked because they happen to be on the same topic. • Points might be put in a list, but not necessarily in any sort of order of importance.
• Paragraphs might be used to show some of the obvious different topics in the writing.

1 mark

Band B2

• Paragraphs usually start with the main topic in the first sentence. • The paragraphs will contain examples. • The letter has some opening and closing comments, but they will be fairly brief and undeveloped.

2 marks

Band B3

• Paragraphs are written in a logical order. • The introduction and conclusion are clear. • Paragraphs of different lengths are used, e.g. short paragraphs might take the form of a persuasive question.

3 marks

Band B4

• Detailed content is well handled within and between paragraphs. • Some phrases like 'On the other hand' or 'In addition to this', etc. are used to link the paragraphs. • The introduction and conclusion to the letter are developed and help to make it more persuasive.

4 marks

Band B5

• Paragraphs are varied in length to suit the different ideas being discussed.
• The paragraphs are linked with a variety of words and phrases. • Paragraphs
are ordered in such a way that the writer might have used them to highlight
contrasts, or to be ironic.

5 marks

Section C: Composition and effect

This section focuses on the overall impact of the writing and the effect it has on
the reader.

Band C1

• The letter shows some awareness of the reader. • There is some relevant
content, but it might be uneven, e.g. more about why the market is personally
important than why it is important to the community.

1–3 marks

Band C2

• The letter is generally lively and attempts to interest the reader. • The content
of the letter shows that the writer recognises its purpose. • Some reasons are
given for the ideas and opinions, but perhaps not that many.

4–6 marks

Band C3

• The letter is detailed and gives clear reasons for the opinions and viewpoints
expressed. • The letter engages the reader's interest. • The letter gives a range
of relevant ideas and the writer's viewpoint is clear.

7–9 marks

Band C4

• The letter is well written because it uses a range of techniques such as
repetition, humour and a consideration of the reader's needs in order to
persuade. • The writer's view is consistent.

10–12 marks

Band C5

• The tone and content of the letter are appropriate and well judged. • The letter
deliberately interacts with the reader. • Content is relevant throughout and is
used to support the persuasive ideas, e.g. to persuade the council to change its
plan to demolish the street market through relevant economic, cultural and social
considerations.

13–15 marks

Paper 3: Section A: Shorter Writing Task
Pages 26–28

The bands give descriptions of the main features to look out for. In section F, simply choose the band (and mark) that 'best fits' your writing. You will notice that bands in sections D and E have different numbers of marks.

For D1 and D2: satisfying two or three of the criteria achieves the lower mark in the band. You must satisfy all four of the criteria in the band, e.g. D2, and fewer than half the criteria in the band above, to achieve the higher mark in the band, e.g. 4.

For E1: you must show evidence of all three criteria but nothing higher to get the one mark.

For all other D and E bands:

- If your writing satisfies half or more but not all of the criteria for a particular band, give yourself the lowest marks available for that band.

- If your writing satisfies all the criteria for a band (e.g. E2) but none of the criteria for the band above, give yourself the middle mark for that band (e.g. 3).

- If your writing satisfies all the criteria for a band (e.g. E2) and fewer than half of the criteria for the band above, give yourself the full marks for your band (e.g. 4).

Write the marks you have achieved in the Marking grid on page 55.

It is important to look at sections D to F in order to build up an accurate overall picture of the strengths and weaknesses of your writing. For example you might create good effects in your writing (section E), but you might need to improve your spelling (section F). By looking at your scores in every section, you should be able to see in which areas of your writing you need to improve.

Section D: Sentence structure/punctuation and text organisation

This section focuses on how you choose to organise your writing and how this contributes to its overall effect.

Band D1

• Sentences are fairly simple. • Sentences are linked by simple joining words like 'and' or 'then'. • Full stops and capital letters are used with accuracy.
• Paragraphs are used to separate the more obvious different topics given in the task.

1–2 marks

Band D2

• Sentences are varied and use linking words like 'who' or 'which'. • The writing is written in the same tense throughout. • Words like 'he', 'she', 'it, 'they' and other pronouns are generally used correctly. • Paragraphs are mainly put into a logical order, as is the detail within them.

3–4 marks

Band D3

• A variety of longer sentences are used. This includes those that have been built up from joining simpler ones together to make longer ones and sentences where the word order has been successfully re-arranged for effect. • Words like 'completely', 'partly' and others which help to make meaning more precise are used. • Words like 'he', 'she', 'it', 'they' and other pronouns are used correctly. • Tenses are used correctly. • Paragraphs are used for appropriate reasons and are put into a logical order. • The detail in them is put into a logical order.

5–7 marks

Band D4

• Sentences are written in a variety of ways to achieve interesting effects that suit the purpose of the writing. • A range of punctuation is used – sometimes to create effects. • Paragraphs are of different lengths and the information in them is organised cleverly to suit what is being written about.

8–10 marks

Section E: Composition and effect

This section focuses on the overall impact of your writing and how well it fits the audience you are writing for.

Band E1

• The description shows some awareness of the reader. • Simple techniques, like repetition, are used, to describe the key features of the place chosen. • Content is relevant to the question, but might well be unevenly used, e.g. too much description of what is seen and not enough appropriate use of other senses.

1 mark

Band E2

• The description tries to interest the reader. • Some techniques, e.g. use of adjectives, are used to help descriptions, but they might not be very imaginative.

2–4 marks

Band E3

• The writer interests the reader. • The writer is clearly aware of what type of writing he/she is doing and for whom. • Descriptions are developed to help to create a mood or setting. • The tone of the writing is consistent throughout.

5–7 marks

Band E4

• The description is well written and convincing throughout. • The writer really engages the reader's interest. • There is a very good range of well chosen details. • The viewpoint of the writer is consistent throughout.

8–10 marks

Section F: Spelling

This section focuses on accuracy in spelling. Choose the section that best fits your writing.

Band F1

• Simple words are usually accurate.

1 mark

Band F2

• Simple words and those with more than one or two syllables are generally accurate.

2 marks

Band F3

• More complicated words that fit to regular patterns and rules are generally accurate.

3 marks

Band F4

• Most spelling, including irregular words, is accurate.

4 marks

Band F5

• Virtually all spelling, including complex words that don't fit to regular rules or patterns, is correct.

5 marks

Paper 3: Section B: Reading Task
Pages 29–35

Macbeth

In your study of *Macbeth* at school, you will have looked at the scenes chosen here in detail. In the actual test, there will be gobbets (small sections – here about 50 lines) of text in the question booklet. You will need to focus on the words in **these** extracts. The extracts are not intended to be dealt with to the exclusion of all else, but to provide the focus/framework for your answer. If you can think of other things from the scenes to add to support your answer, write them down! Underneath you will find lots of different points that you COULD have included in your answer. Do not expect to have thought of them all! Remember, you only have 45 minutes to answer. They are all written here so that you can 'revise' them after you have answered the question.

The scenes you need to read are in the pull-out section at the back of this book.

What we learn about Macbeth's desires – Act 1 Scene 3

- "By Sinel's death I know I am thane of Glamis;
  But how of Cawdor?" – this shows us that Macbeth's curiosity has been
  alerted by the witches' predictions.

- "to be king
  Stands not within the prospect of belief," – this shows, that at this point, he
  can hardly believe that he could become king.

- "Speak, I charge you." – the fact that he is ordering the witches to speak shows
  his anxiety and eagerness to find out more.

- "Your children shall be kings." – at this point, his desires haven't affected his
  relationship with Banquo, because he's still interested in the fact that his
  friend has been promised good things too.

- "And thane of Cawdor too: went it not so? " – here, the fact that he is repeating
  the ideas to himself, shows that he is still coming to terms with the fact that
  the predictions might come true.

- "The thane of Cawdor lives: why do you dress me
  In borrow'd robes?" – this shows his continuing amazement and his shock
  that the prediction may be starting to come true.

- "Glamis, and thane of Cawdor!
  The greatest is behind." – at this point the audience are starting to see a glimpse
  of Macbeth's deeper thoughts. By referring to "the greatest" we see that he
  feels that the biggest obstacle towards him becoming king, at this point in time,
  has gone.

- "Do you not hope your children shall be kings,
  When those that gave the thane of Cawdor to me
  Promised no less to them?" – here, Macbeth's desire to become king is not
  yet fully developed, because he is still at times talking openly to Banquo and
  sharing his ambitious thoughts, not plotting against him.

- "This supernatural soliciting
  Cannot be ill, cannot be good:" – in this aside, Macbeth shows that he is still
  uncertain within himself. He is trying to weigh up whether the predictions are a
  good or bad thing.

- "BANQUO

  Look, how our partner's rapt." – Banquo's comment reveals to the audience that Macbeth is lost in his thoughts. If he is so wrapped up in the idea of becoming king that others notice, he must be seriously affected.

- "let us speak

  Our free hearts each to other." – again, Macbeth's ambition has not yet grown so great that it has affected his relationship with Banquo. If it had, then he would have been more reluctant to discuss these matters with him.

What we learn about Macbeth's desires – Act 3 Scene 1

- "To be thus is nothing;

  But to be safely thus.–Our fears in Banquo

  Stick deep " – In this scene we see how Macbeth's greed and ambition have grown, so much so that he does not now trust his former friend Banquo.

- "There is none but he

  Whose being I do fear:" – as he is getting more ambitious, he is getting more arrogant. He says that he only fears Banquo and no-one else.

- "He chid the sisters

  When first they put the name of king upon me," – In saying this, Macbeth is showing that he is making up excuses to justify his own behaviour to himself. He makes out that Banquo's comments were somehow indicated disloyalty.

- "If 't be so,

  For Banquo's issue have I filed my mind" – Macbeth's increasing desire is turning him against Banquo. He feels that killing Duncan will be in vain if it means that Banquo's and not his sons, reap the benefit of being kings in future.

- "Ay, in the catalogue ye go for men;

  As hounds and greyhounds, mongrels, spaniels, curs,

  Shoughs, water-rugs and demi-wolves, are clept

  All by the name of dogs:" – Macbeth is talking to the murderers that he has hired to kill Banquo. The way that he describes them, comparing them to dogs, shows how his increasing greed for power is reducing his respect for human life.

- "every minute of his being thrusts

  Against my near'st of life:" – this comment shows how Macbeth's desires are getting more evil. His former friend is now seen as a threat who must be killed. The desire for power is corrupting Macbeth more and more.

Make sure that you comment on both of the scenes in your answer. If you only comment on one scene, the examiner will knock marks off, no matter how good your answer is on the other scene.

To get the higher marks on this question, make some comparison between the scenes.

To determine your level, see the criteria below. Choose the level description that best fits your answer.

LEVEL 4	A few simple comments are made about Macbeth, retelling parts of the scenes and possibly making simple comments about his desires. The answers may only be partly relevant. References may be made to the text but there may not be an explanation.
LEVEL 5	An answer is given which is a straightforward commentary on the scene. This may offer an overview of the scenes showing some understanding about Macbeth's desires although the ideas may be undeveloped. Points are referenced to the text, or words spoken by the characters.
LEVEL 6	A focused answer is given, with a degree of exploration of the text. A detailed commentary is made, showing some understanding of Macbeth's desires. There is some awareness of the language used and how this indicates Macbeth's desires to become king. References to the text are relevant and appropriate.
LEVEL 7	A reasonably full answer is given which shows knowledge and understanding of the text, characters and language. A detailed commentary is made, which shows an understanding of the way that language used contributes to the exploration of Macbeth's character and desires. The answer shows real insight into the character of Macbeth . Comments are justified by carefully selected reference to the text.
Gifted and Talented	If you are working consistently at the top end of Level 7 and above you are achieving in the "Gifted and Talented" range.

See page 54 ("Determining your level") to work out your overall Reading Level.

Twelfth Night

Many characters in *Twelfth Night* wear disguises, beginning with Viola, who puts on 'male' clothing and pretends to be a boy. The play raises questions about what makes us who we are. It makes the audience wonder if it is what we are (man or woman, rich nobleman or ordinary person) that makes us act the way we do, or whether it is what other people see, and the way they then treat us, that makes us act the way we do.

In your study of *Twelfth Night* at school, you will have looked at the scenes chosen here in detail. In the actual test, there will be gobbets (small sections – here about 50 lines) of text in the question booklet. You will need to focus on the words in **these** extracts. The extracts are not intended to be dealt with to the exclusion of all else, but to provide the focus/framework for your answer. If you can think of other things from the scenes to add to support your answer, write them down! Underneath you will find lots of different points that you COULD have included in your answer. Do not expect to have thought of them all! Remember, you only have 45 minutes to answer. They are all written here so that you can 'revise' them after you have answered the question.

The scenes you need to read are in the pull-out section at the back of this book.

Useful quotations from Act 2 Scene 3

- "I hate it as an unfilled can.
  To be up after midnight and to go to bed then, is
  early: so that to go to bed after midnight is to go
  to bed betimes"
  – by talking in riddles, Sir Toby is making us question what is real and what is not, which is one of the important themes in the play, closely linked to the use of disguises.

- SIR TOBY BELCH:
  "Does not our life consist of the
  four elements?"

- SIR ANDREW
  "Faith, so they say; but I think it rather consists
  of eating and drinking."

  – Sir Andrew's reply here shows us one of the uses of humour – to bring people down to earth and to deflate pomposity.

- "I had rather than forty shillings I had such a leg,
  and so sweet a breath to sing, as the fool has." – the humour in Sir Andrew's
  comment is cruel, showing another of its purposes – to insult people.

- CLOWN
  "Would you have a love-song, or a song of good life?" – even a simple
  comment like this shows us what Shakespeare believes - that love is more
  important than anything."

- "What is love? 'tis not hereafter;
  Present mirth hath present laughter;
  What's to come is still unsure:" – in the Clown's song, there is a great deal of
  serious comment on the nature of love. Here we see that although love is
  important, it is very uncertain. We have to enjoy the moment, because the
  nature of love makes it very difficult to judge how people will feel in the future.

- "Youth's a stuff will not endure." – in the same song, the Clown is also telling
  us that it is best to enjoy the physical side of love while you're young, because
  you will soon be too old and incapable of enjoying it.

- SIR ANDREW
  "A mellifluous voice, as I am true knight" – another function of humour that we
  see is to make fun of ourselves, as Sir Andrew does here.

- SIR ANDREW
  "Tis not the first time I have constrained one to
  call me knave. Begin, fool: it begins 'Hold thy peace.'"

- CLOWN
  "I shall never begin if I hold my peace." – the pun on the word "peace" here
  shows that Shakespeare used crude double entendres to simply entertain the
  audience and create characters that the Elizabethans could easily relate to.

Useful Quotations from Act 4 Scene 2
- CLOWN
  "Well, I'll put it on, and I will dissemble myself in't;" – in this scene, the clown
  is disguising himself in order to question Malvolio. Shakespeare uses disguise
  as a way of getting people to reveal the truth about themselves, either
  intentionally or unintentionally. This raises the issue of what a person's true
  identity is.

- MALVOLIO
  "Who calls there?"

- CLOWN
  Sir Topas the curate, who comes to visit Malvolio
  "the lunatic." – Shakespeare is using dramatic irony here (The audience know what is going on, but Malvolio doesn't). By making the Clown into a respectable curate and Malvolio into a lunatic, the audience are forced to question what is reality and what is appearance, which are important issue throughout the play.

- CLOWN
  "Madman, thou errest: I say, there is no darkness
  but ignorance;" – Shakespeare puts wisdom into the mouths of people we wouldn't expect to be wise. He does this to make the audience again question what is real, what is wisdom and what is not. He is forcing them to keep an open mind and not judge too quickly.

- "I am no more mad than
  you are:" – Malvolio's words are double-edged. Again this is thought-provoking, because the audience have to decide how we judge madness and sanity. Shakespeare is using the idea of appearances to do this.

Make sure that you comment on both of the scenes in your answer. If you only comment on one scene, the examiner will knock marks off, no matter how good your answer is on the other scene.

To get the higher marks on this question, make some comparison between the scenes.

To determine your level, see the criteria below. Choose the level description that best fits your answer.

LEVEL 4
A few simple comments are made about the scenes, retelling parts of the scenes and possibly making simple comments about some of the ideas raised in them. The answers may only be partly relevant. References may be made to the text but there may not be an explanation.

LEVEL 5
An answer is given which is a straightforward commentary on the scene. This may offer an overview of the scenes showing some understanding about the ideas that Shakespeare raises, although the ideas may be undeveloped. Points are referenced to the text, or words spoken by the characters.

LEVEL 6
A focused answer is given, with a degree of exploration of the text. A detailed commentary is made, showing some understanding of the themes and ideas raised. There is some awareness of the language used and how this contributes to the ideas that Shakespeare is putting across. References to the text are relevant and appropriate.

LEVEL 7
A reasonably full answer is given which shows knowledge and understanding of the text, characters and language. A detailed commentary is made, which shows an understanding of the way that language used contributes to the exploration of the important themes in the play. The answer shows real insight into the themes and ideas of the play as revealed in these scenes.. Comments are justified by carefully selected reference to the text.

Gifted and Talented
If you are working consistently at the top end of Level 7 and above you are achieving in the "Gifted and Talented" range.

See page 54 ("Determining your level") to work out your overall Reading Level.

Determining your level

FINDING YOUR LEVEL IN PAPERS 1, 2 AND 3

When you have marked a test, enter the total number of marks you scored for each question on the marking grid on the next page. Then add them up and enter the test total on the grid.

Using the total for each test, look at the charts below to determine the level for each test.

Paper 1

Reading Paper

Below level 4	Level 4	Level 5	Level 6	Level 7
0–8	9–19	20–29	30–40	41–50

If you are working consistently at the top end of level 7, you are achieving in the 'Gifted and Talented' range.

Paper 2

Writing Paper

Below level 4	Level 4	Level 5	Level 6	Level 7
0–5	6–10	11–15	16–20	21–25

If you are working consistently at the top end of level 7, you are achieving in the 'Gifted and Talented' range.

Paper 3

Reading Task

Look at the 'best match' in the mark scheme and choose the level description that describes your answers most accurately.

Writing Task

Below level 4	Level 4	Level 5	Level 6	Level 7
0–4	5–10	11–17	18–24	24–25

If you are working consistently at the top end of level 7, you are achieving in the 'Gifted and Talented' range.

FINDING YOUR OVERALL LEVEL IN ENGLISH

Look at the levels you have achieved in each paper, taking an average to estimate the level you are currently working at in Reading/Writing. If there are particular areas where you do not score as well, read the relevant part of the paper again (together with the answers) to see how you can improve your work.

Marking grid

Paper 1: Reading Paper Pages 11–21

Section	Marks available	Marks scored
Fairtrade Fortnight 2002	17	15
A Sheep Fair	14	
Saturday in Sydney Street	19	
TOTAL	**50**	

Paper 2: Writing Paper Pages 22–24

Section	Marks available	Marks scored
A Sentence structure and punctuation	5	
B Text structure and organisation	5	
C Composition and effect	15	
TOTAL	**25**	

Paper 3: Section A: Writing Task Pages 26–28

Section	Marks available	Marks scored
D Sentence structure/punctuation and text organisation	10	
E Composition and effect	10	
F Spelling	5	
TOTAL	**25**	

Paper 3: Section B: Reading Task Pages 29–35

Section	Level achieved
Macbeth	
Twelfth Night	

National Curriculum

Key Stage 3 Age 13–14

Practice Papers

Key Stage 3
National Tests

MATHS

How the Key Stage 3 National Tests will affect your education

- All students in Year 9 (age 13–14) will take National Tests in English, Mathematics and Science. These important tests are held in May each year and are designed to be an objective assessment of the work you will have done during Key Stage 3 (Years 7–9) of the National Curriculum.

- You will also have your school work assessed by your teachers. These teacher assessments will be set alongside your results in the National Tests to give a clear picture of your overall achievement.

- In July, the test results together with the teacher assessments will be reported to parents/guardians.

- The results may be used by your teacher to help place you in the appropriate teaching group for some GCSE courses next year.

How this book will help your education

- This book offers plenty of practice in the type of question you will face in the Key Stage 3 National Test for Mathematics, including Mental Mathematics.

- The answers and a mark scheme have been provided to allow you to check how you have done.

- The 'Examiner's tip' boxes in the Answers section give you advice on how to improve your answers and avoid common mistakes.

- A unique Marking grid allows you to record your results and estimate the level of the National Curriculum at which you are working.

KS3 Maths Contents

What you need to know about the National Tests

What is the purpose of National Tests?

The tests, taken by students in Year 9, have several functions:

- they provide the government with a snapshot picture of attainment throughout the country, enabling it to make judgements about whether standards are improving nationally;

- they give information to OFSTED about schools achievements, so that they can judge which schools are improving and which are deemed to be failing their students;

- they give you information about your progress compared to national standards;

- they may be used by teachers to place you in the appropriate teaching group for the GCSE courses starting in Year 10.

How do the tests work?

In May of Year 9, you will take tests on the core subjects of English, Mathematics and Science. In Maths the written tests are grouped into four ranges of levels called 'tiers'. The four tiers cover levels 3–5, 4–6, 5–7 and 6–8. Each tier has two written test papers, the first of which must be completed without the use of a calculator, together with a Mental Mathematics test. The tests are not marked in school by a teacher, but posted off to an external marker, who

is often a teacher in another school or a retired teacher. External markers have been trained in marking the tests so that all students' test papers throughout the country are marked to the same standard.

Once the tests have been marked, the mark is translated into a 'level'. The level that each mark corresponds to is decided according to results gained in pre-tests and the tests themselves. It varies slightly from year to year. The test papers, marks and levels are returned to your school in July. The levels are then reported to your parents/guardians.

What do the tests assess?

The tests are designed to assess your knowledge, skills and understanding in the context of the programme of study set out in the National Curriculum. This can be found on the National Curriculum website, www.nc.uk.net. The programme of study is divided into four sections, called Attainment Targets:

- Ma1 – Using and applying Mathematics
- Ma2 – Number and algebra
- Ma3 – Shape, space and measures
- Ma4 – Handling data

Questions in the tests cover all four Attainment Targets, but the questions assessing Ma1 are usually set within the context of one of the other Attainment Targets.

What are the levels and what do they mean?

There is a set of benchmark standards that measure a student's progress through the first three Key Stages of the National Curriculum. Attainment is measured in steps called 'levels', from 1 to 8. The National Curriculum document sets out the knowledge, skills and understanding that students should demonstrate at each level. The government target is for students to achieve level 2 at the end of Key Stage 1, level 4 at the end of Key Stage 2 and level 5 or 6 at the end of Key Stage 3. The chart below shows these government targets.

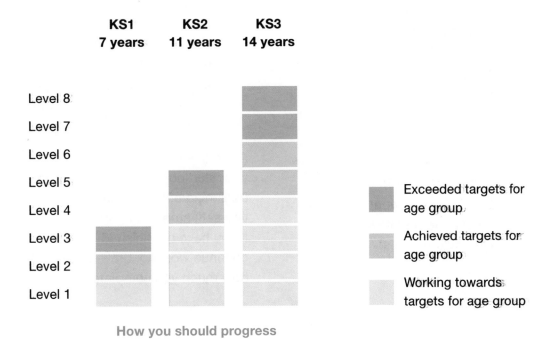

How you should progress

Preparing and practising for the Maths Test

The questions in this book test the same things as the actual test papers:

- knowledge
- understanding
- handling information
- interpretation and evaluation
- solving problems.

What are the key features of this book?

This book contains all you need to prepare for the tests:

- National Curriculum requirements – key information for each of the Attainment Targets Ma1, Ma2, Ma3 and Ma4.
- Questions – one non-calculator and one calculator practice test paper for both levels 4–6 and levels 5–7, a non-calculator paper for levels 6–8 and two Mental Mathematics papers. This means that you will find plenty of questions to practise, regardless of which tier you are entered for.
- Answers – showing the responses that will gain credit in the tests and how the marks are allocated.
- Examiner's tips – advice on how to improve your performance.
- Level charts – what the marks mean in terms of National Curriculum levels.

How should I use this book?

Try taking Tests A and B first, on different days. Mark each test to see how you have done. If your results indicate that you are working at Level 5 or higher, then you should try Tests C and D, which are more challenging, some time later. Work through the answers and advice to see where you might have done better on Tests A and B. When you've had a chance to improve your understanding, take Tests C and D on different days. The **Letts Key Stage 3 Success** range shown on the back cover is our recommended revision source.

First, make sure that you have:

- read the instructions on page 11;
- all the equipment on page 8;
- revised all the commonly used formulae, e.g. for a circle $C = 2\pi r$, $A = \pi r^2$, and Pythagoras' theorem $a^2 + b^2 = c^2$. The only formulae you will be given are listed for you on page 8 and may be referred to during the written tests but **not** during the mental tests.
- a quiet room in which to work, where you will be comfortable and will not be disturbed.

Allow one hour to take each test. Note your starting time in the box at the beginning of the test and time yourself; stop writing after 60 minutes. If you have not finished but wish to continue working, draw a line to show how much you completed within the test time, then continue for as long as you wish. You are allowed to ask an adult to explain the meaning of words you do not understand, provided that they are not mathematical terms such as 'quadrilateral'. Some questions set in the National Tests now require you show that you are 'Using and applying Mathematics' (Attainment Target Ma1). These questions are indicated with a diamond (◆).

After completing the test, work through the paper along with the answers and advice at the back of the book. It is a good idea to highlight or make a note of areas where you do not do well, so that you can revise these at a later stage. Record your marks in the top half of the boxes in the margin. You will also see subtotal boxes at the bottom of each section of the test – you can keep a running total there. If you required extra time to complete the test, do not count the marks for the 'extra' questions in your final score.

Work out the total marks gained for each question, write them in the grid on page 79 and add them up to get the total mark for the paper. Then use the charts on page 78 to determine the level of your performance on each test as well as an overall level.

Mental Mathematics is an important part of the National Curriculum and there is a separate Mental Mathematics Test in addition to the two written papers.

The test assesses your mental recall

and ability to deal with numerical problems, and it counts for 20% of the final mark.

Two Mental Mathematics Tests are included on pages 59 and 60 of this book. You should detach these pages and get someone to read out each question twice to you. You will then have 5, 10 or 15 seconds to complete your answer, which should be written on the answer sheets (pages 57–58).

If you achieve at least level 6 in Tests A–D, you should try Test E, which is intended to assess levels 6–8. This test should also take 60 minutes. Again, total your marks on the Marking grid and work out your level using the chart on page 78.

What does the level mean?

The tests in this book give a guide as to the level that you are likely to achieve in the actual tests. We hope that, through practice, these tests will give you the confidence to achieve your best. By working through the answers and notes, you should be able to improve your achievement.

How do I prepare to take the actual tests?

A few days before the test:

- work through some practice questions, making sure that you understand which answers are correct and why;
- check that you know which test papers you will be taking and when these are to be sat;
- double check that you have all the necessary equipment.

Above all, don't worry too much! Although the National Tests are important, your achievement throughout the school year is equally important. Do your best in these tests; that is all that anyone can ask.

Equipment you will need

The following equipment may be needed for answering these questions:

- a pen, pencil and rubber;
- a ruler (a 30 cm plastic ruler is most suitable);
- a calculator (an inexpensive four-function calculator is all that is required. Do not use a scientific calculator that has too many complicated functions);
- an angle measurer (this is probably easier to use than a protractor, particularly for angles greater than 180°).

- tracing paper (this is useful for rotational symmetry questions);

- a pair of compasses (use this for drawing circles);

- a mirror (this is useful for symmetry questions).

Formulae you will need

Area of a trapezium

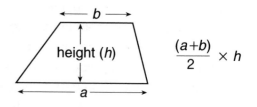

$$\frac{(a+b)}{2} \times h$$

Volume of a prism

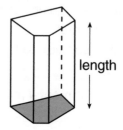

area of cross section × length

National Curriculum requirements

Ma1 Using and applying Mathematics: Requirements at each level

Level 4 Develop strategies for solving problems; apply mathematics to practical situations. Present information and results in a clear and organised way.

Level 5 Identify and obtain information needed to solve problems. Check whether results are sensible. Describe situations mathematically, using symbols, words and diagrams. Draw conclusions and explain reasoning.

Level 6 Solve complex problems by breaking them down. Interpret information in a variety of forms. Explain use of diagrams and give mathematical justifications.

Level 7 Refine and extend the mathematics used to give fuller solutions. Explain and give reasons for form of presentation used. Justify generalisations, arguments and solutions.

Level 8 Follow alternative approaches and use a range of mathematical techniques. Use symbols precisely and consistently. Comment constructively on reasoning and results.

Gifted and Talented Indicates exceptional performance at level 8.

Ma2 Number and algebra: Requirements at each level

Level 4 Understand place value; multiply and divide whole numbers by 10 and 100. Use mental recall of multiplication facts up to 10×10. Use efficient written methods of addition, subtraction, multiplication and division. Add, subtract and order decimals. Check answers for reasonableness. Use simple fractions and percentages. Recognise and describe number patterns and use formulae in words. Use simple coordinates.

Level 5 Multiply and divide by 10, 100 and 1000. Add, subtract and order negative numbers and work with decimals. Simplify fractions and solve problems involving ratio and proportion. Calculate fractional and percentage parts, with and without a calculator. Use non-calculator methods to multiply and divide. Check solutions by reversing the operation or approximating. Use simple formulae and brackets. Use and interpret coordinates.

Level 6 Order and approximate decimals. Solve problems involving comparisons, giving one number as a fraction or percentage of another. Use equivalence between fractions, decimals and percentages and work with ratios. Add and subtract fractions. Find rules for number sequences and solve linear equations. Draw graphs on coordinate diagrams.

Level 7 Use one significant figure estimates. Use a calculator efficiently and appropriately. Calculate proportional changes. Use algebra and graphical methods to solve simultaneous equations. Solve simple inequalities.

Level 8 Calculate with powers, roots and numbers in standard form. Solve problems involving repeated proportional change. Evaluate and manipulate algebraic formulae and expressions; find common factors; multiply out brackets. Solve inequalities and interpret graphs, including those that model real life situations.

Gifted and Talented Indicates exceptional performance at level 8.

Ma3 Shape, space and measures: Requirements at each level

Level 4 Draw 2-D shapes on grids. Reflect shapes in mirror lines. Read a variety of scales. Find simple perimeters and areas.

Level 5 Measure and draw angles to nearest degree. Know the angle sums in a triangle and at a point. Identify symmetries. Know rough metric equivalents of imperial units still in use and convert between metric units. Make sensible estimations in everyday situations. Use formula for area of a triangle.

Level 6 Use 2-D representations of 3-D objects. Classify quadrilaterals and solve problems involving angle and symmetry properties of polygons, intersecting and parallel lines and explain these. Find circumference and area of circles, areas of plane figures and volume of cuboids. Draw enlargements of shapes.

Level 7 Use Pythagoras' theorem. Calculate lengths, areas and volumes in plane shapes and prisms. Find the locus of an object according to a rule. Understand error in measurement and use compound measures.

Level 8 Use congruence and similarity and sine, cosine and tangent in right-angled triangles when solving problems.

Gifted and Talented Indicates exceptional performance at level 8.

Ma4 Handling data: Requirements at each level

Level 4 Collect and record data using a frequency table. Use mode and range. Group data and represent these in frequency diagrams. Interpret frequency diagrams and simple line graphs.

Level 5 Find mean of discrete data and compare two distributions, using range, mode, median or mean. Interpret graphs and diagrams and draw conclusions. Use probability scale from 0 to 1 and find probabilities based on equally likely outcomes or experimental evidence.

Level 6 Collect and record continuous data and create grouped frequency tables. Construct frequency diagrams and pie charts. Understand correlation and draw conclusions from scatter diagrams. Identify all the outcomes of combined experiments and represent these. Use the fact that the total probability of all the mutually exclusive outcomes of an experiment is 1.

Level 7 Find the modal class and estimate the mean, median and range of sets of grouped data. Compare distributions and make inferences based on measures of average and range. Draw a line of best fit on a scatter diagram. Use relative frequency as an estimate of probability.

Level 8 Use cumulative frequency tables and diagrams to estimate median and interquartile range; compare and make inferences. Calculate the probability of a compound event.

Gifted and Talented Indicates exceptional performance at level 8.

Instructions

Each test should take 60 minutes. Enter your start and finish times in the boxes at the beginning of each test.

Try to answer all of the questions.

Read the questions carefully. If you think, after reading a question carefully, that you cannot answer it, leave it and come back to it later.

The questions you have to answer are given in blue boxes. For example:

How many 3 litre cans does Asif have to buy to cover an area of 254 square metres?

Write your answers and working on the test papers in this book.

The ✎ shows where you should answer the question. The lines or space given should give you some indication of what is expected.

Look at the number of marks for each part of a question. This is shown in a box in the margin, for example:

There is also a box showing the maximum number of marks for each section. You can write in your subtotal, so that you can see at a glance how you are doing.

In Mathematics, marks are awarded for the method you use as well as the answer. It is important to show your working clearly so you can receive credit.

You must not use a calculator in Tests A, C or E, but a calculator may be used in Tests B and D.

Look carefully at the words you write, particularly mathematical words. Read your answers carefully to yourself and make sure you have clearly expressed what you mean.

GOOD LUCK!

Test A
Levels 4–6

START

FINISH

WITHOUT CALCULATOR

1 Below is a list of mathematical words.

Use suitable words from this list to complete the sentences below.

cube factor integer multiple square square root sum

a 45 is a .... of 5.

b 49 is the .... of 7.

c 3 is a .... of 81.

2 Here are some wall tiles.
Draw in all the lines of symmetry.

a
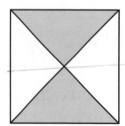

b
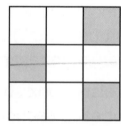

c

d
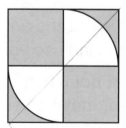

3 Show the probabilities of these events on the probability line.

Mark each with an arrow and its letter.

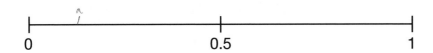

| 0 | 0.5 | 1 |

a If I throw an ordinary dice, the number will be odd.

b If I throw an ordinary dice, I shall get a 6.

c It will snow in London on 1st August next year.

d The next king will be a man.

1
Q3a

1
Q3b

1
Q3c

1
Q3d

4 Below are various shapes.

Identify the shape that is similar to the shaded shape, and the shape that is congruent to the shaded shape.

◆
2
Q4

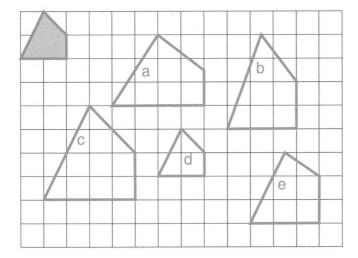

Shape .... is similar.

Shape .... is congruent.

5 Chuck is an American visiting France.
He needs a new shirt.

This formula shows you how to work out the French
sizes for given American sizes.

> French size is twice
> the American size
> plus 9.

a Find the French size for American size 17.

b Write a formula for the French size (F) in terms of the
American size (A).

c Chuck bought a French size 37.
What is the American size?

6 Look at the equations below.
Fill in the missing numbers.

a $43 \times 10 =$ ....

b $6200 \div 100 =$ ....

c .... × 100 = 7000

d 21 000 ÷ .... = 210

e 830 × .... = 830 000

f 940 ÷ 100 = ...

g 0.026 × .... = 2.6

h .... ÷ 1000 = 0.38

7 Eric measured his desk. It was 65 cm deep and 1 metre 7 cm wide.

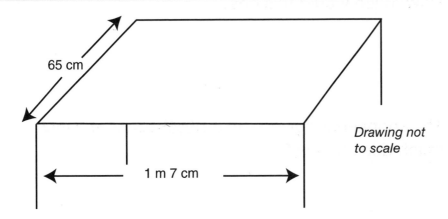

65 cm

1 m 7 cm

Drawing not to scale

a Write the measurements in

(i) millimetres ....

(ii) metres ....

b Roughly, how many feet are these measurements?

Max. 15
Qs 5–7
subtotal

....

15

8 Here are the results of tests on two brands of torch battery.
Which would you buy? Give a reason.

	Mean	**Range**
Brand A	15 hours	3.5 hours
Brand B	14 hours	1.7 hours

....

....

9 Bob is having a barbecue with his friends.
He wants to buy 45 tins of baked beans at 17p a tin.

a How much would this cost?

....

b The shopkeeper gives him a 20% discount. How much does he pay?

....

10 a Look at the expression below.
Simplify it.

$2c + 3d - c + 4d$

....

16

b What must you add to $3x + 2y$ to get $5x - 2y$?

c Find the value of $5x - 2y$ when $x = 3$ and $y = -4$.

d Solve these equations.

(i) $\frac{x}{3} = 10$

(ii) $3x + 10 = 7$

11 Here are 5 number cards.

 | 2 | 4 | 5 | 5 | 8 |

Use all the cards to make an addition sum that has the answer 600.

+

6 0 0

Max. 15
Qs 8–11 subtotal

17

12 Gill has three spinners to use in a game.
Here is the first. It is unbiased.

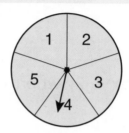

a The arrow is spun once.

(i) What is the probability that it lands on 4?

....

(ii) What is the probability that it lands on an odd number?

....

b The second spinner is biased.
Here are the results of 10 spins.

Result	1	2	3	4	5
Number of times	1	2	1	1	5

(i) Explain why the probability of getting a 2 need not be 0.2.

....

....

Here are the results of 100 spins.

Result	1	2	3	4	5
Number of times	10	23	21	16	30

(ii) What is the probability that on the next spin the arrow will land on 2?

1
Q12b(ii)

....

c The third spinner also has five numbers.
Here are some of the probabilities.

Result	1	2	3	4	5
Probability	0.1	0.3	0.1		0.25

(i) What is the probability of the arrow landing on 4?

1
Q12c(i)

....

(ii) What is the probability that it will not land on 5?

1
Q12c(ii)

....

Max. 6
Q 12
subtotal

2

Q13a

13 a This year, the local football club raised £750 for charity.

It is to be shared between *Age Concern* and *Save the Children* in the ratio 2:3.

How much does each charity get?

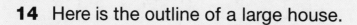

1

Q13b

b Last year, the football club only raised £600.

What was the percentage increase this year?

14 Here is the outline of a large house.

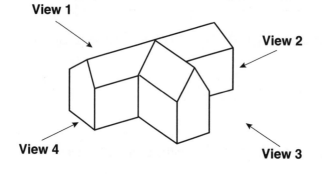

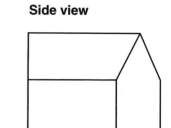

Side view

1

Q14a

◆

a Look at the side view of the house.
From which direction is it drawn?

3

Q14b

◆

b Sketch the view of the house from above.

15 These pie charts show information from a survey about computers at home. In the survey, 500 people in Brighton and 1000 people in Luton were asked about their use of computers at home.

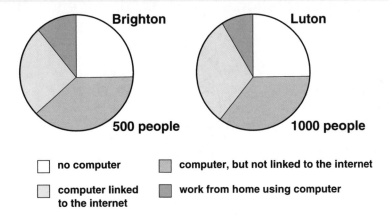

□ no computer   ▨ computer, but not linked to the internet

▨ computer linked to the internet   ▨ work from home using computer

a Roughly what percentage of people in Brighton do not have a computer?

....

b How many people is this?

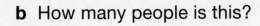

....

Tom said, "The pie charts show that roughly the same number of people in Luton as in Brighton own computers but are not linked to the internet".

c Is this true? Explain your answer.

....

d What is the same in both charts about the number of people who don't own a computer?

Max. 11
Qs
13–15
subtotal

....

Test B
Levels 4–6

START
FINISH

CALCULATOR CAN BE USED

1 Here are some designs for badges.
Write the order of rotational symmetry under each one.

4
Q1

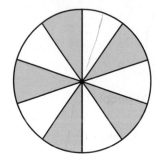

a ....

b ....

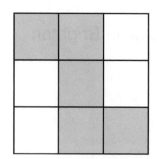

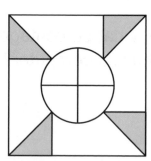

c ....

d ....

2 Melissa has a mobile phone. During the day, calls cost
18p per minute.

a She makes calls for 15 minutes.
How much does this cost?

1
Q2a

£ ...2.7.2..

$\begin{array}{r} {}^{1}8 \\ 15 \\ \hline 90 \\ {}_{1}8 \\ \hline 2.70 \end{array}$

$\begin{array}{r} .62 \\ 6\overline{)372} \end{array}$

b During the evening, calls cost 6p per minute.
How many minutes does she get for £3.72?

1
Q2b

..............62...

22

c Melissa has a £10 phone card to pay for the calls in **a** and **b**.
Work out what value is left on the card after these calls.

1
Q2c

....

d The cost per minute for evening calls is what fraction of the cost per minute for daytime calls?

1
Q2d

....

e On her home phone, the daytime cost is 9p per minute. Find what percentage this cost is of the mobile daytime cost.

1
Q2e

....

f On her home phone, evening calls are 2p per minute. Find how much she could have saved using her home phone for the calls in parts **a** and **b**.

1
Q2f

....

Max. 10
Qs 1–2
subtotal

3 Ranjit has collected data from the students in his class.

Height in centimetres

131	133	137	137	138	139	141	142	142	144
148	149	151	152	152	153	156	156	157	158
158	159	162	162	164	166	167	170	171	174

a What is the median height?

....

b Complete the frequency table.

Height (cm)	Tally	Frequency
130 to 139		
140 to 149		
150 to 159		
160 to 169		
170 to 179		

c Show the information on a frequency diagram.

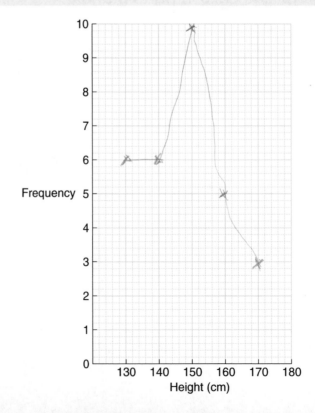

d State the modal group.

....

1
Q3d

This diagram shows the heights of the students in another class.

e Make **two** comparisons with Ranjit's class.

....

....

2
Q3e

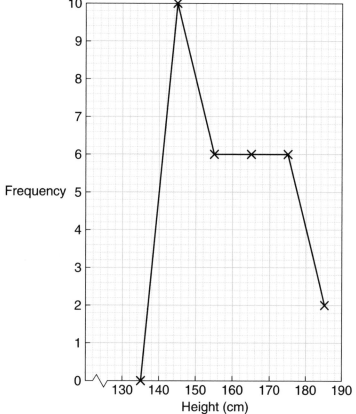

4 The numbers in the circles along each line **add up to the** number in the square on that line.

a Fill in the missing numbers in the square and the circle in the diagram below.

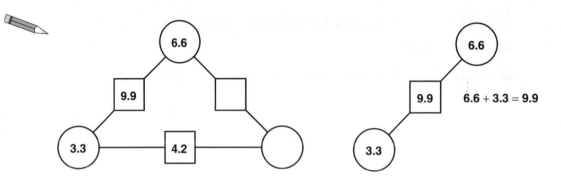

1
Q4a

2
Q4b

b Fill in the missing numbers in this diagram.

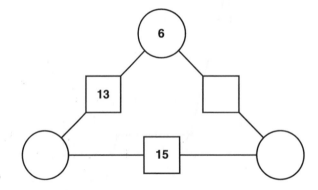

2
Q4c

c Fill in the missing expressions in this diagram.

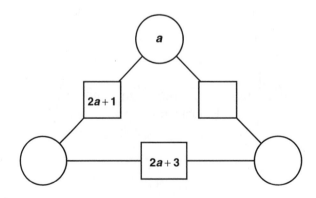

5 Maureen has measured her garden.
Her measurements are shown on the sketch.

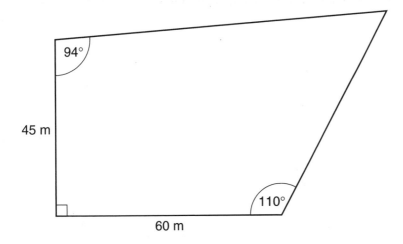

94°

45 m

110°

60 m

a Make an accurate scale drawing of the garden.
Use a scale of 1 cm to 10 m.

◆
4
Q5a

2
Q5b

b Measure the remaining angle and sides.

Max. 11
Qs 4–5
subtotal

2
Q6a(i)

2
Q6a(ii)

6 a Plot the following graphs on the grid below.
   (i) Draw and label the graph of $y = 2x + 1$.
   (ii) Draw and label the graph of $y = 3 - x$.

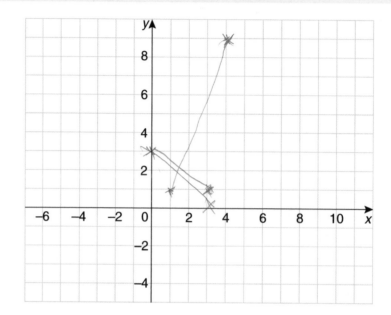

1
Q6b

b Write down the co-ordinates of the point where the two graphs meet.

....

1
Q7a

7 Daljit travels 21 000 miles each year on business.
She gets paid 36p per mile travelling expenses.

a How much will she be paid?

....

1
Q7b

b Her car will use 0.14 litres of fuel for each mile she drives.
How many litres of fuel will she need to buy?

....

c Fuel costs 67.9p per litre.
What is the total cost of the fuel?

£ ....

d Show a rough calculation to check your answer to
part **c**.

....

8 Electrical fuses are sold in the following ratings:

3 amp   5 amp   13 amp

This formula gives the correct fuse to be fitted to an
appliance.

$F = \dfrac{P}{230}$ where F is the fuse in amps and P is the power
rating in watts.

Which fuse should you fit in a hairdryer with a power
rating of 1000 watts?

....

9 Look at questions **a–d** below and on the next page.
Write the name of the quadrilateral described.

a All sides equal, angles not all the same.

....

b Opposite sides equal, all angles equal.

....

Max. 14
Qs 6–9b
subtotal

29

1
Q9c

◆

c Only one pair of opposite sides parallel.

1
Q9d

◆

d Only one diagonal is a line of symmetry.

10 Below is a list of equations to solve.

a $3x - 2 = 7$

1
Q10a

b $4x + 5 = 2x - 7$

2
Q10b

c $7 - x = 2x + 4$

2
Q10c

11 Tom measures the rainfall each day for 10 days. His results in mm are: 2, 0, 0, 1, 7, 11, 5, 2, 0, 0
a What is the range?

1
Q11a

b What is the mode?

1
Q11b

c Calculate the median.

2
Q11c

....

d Calculate the mean.

1
Q11d

....

e Which average gives the best idea of the rainfall during these 10 days? Give a reason for your answer.

◆

1
Q11e

....

12 Prices in a clothes shop are increased by $\frac{2}{5}$.

a What is the new price of a jacket that originally cost £50?

2
Q12a

....

In the sale, the prices are reduced to their original level.

b What percentage reduction is this?

◆

2
Q12b

Max. 17
Qs
9c–12
subtotal

Test C
Levels 5–7

1 This rectangle has 2 axes of symmetry and rotational symmetry of order 2.

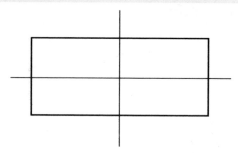

Describe the symmetry of these shapes.

2 / Q1a

a A square

has 4 axes

of symmetry and 4 Rotional
4 Simpetry of order

2 / Q1b

b This hexagon

has 2 axes of symmetry

an rotational symetry 2

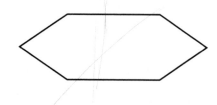

1 / Q1c

c Sketch a shape that has two axes of symmetry and rotational symmetry of order 2 but is not a rectangle.

45 ~~50~~ 0
1 3
——
4 8 7

2 Look at this formula.

$$V = 10t - 13$$

2 ~~3~~ 3
1 3
——
1 7

a Find V when $t = 3$.

.............17..

1
Q2a

b Find the value of t when $V = 50$.

...............4 57...

1
Q2b

3 The number of apples picked from 25 young apple trees was recorded.

25	32	16	23	26
20	33	24	17	13
38	6	20	19	39
13	19	27	16	32
25	48	10	24	29

a Draw a stem-and-leaf diagram for these data.

◆
3
Q3a

1
Q3b

b Find the median number of apples.

....

Max. 11
Qs 1–3
subtotal

33

4 Solve the equations below.

a $2x = 5$

1
Q4a

b $2(x + 3) = 5$

2
Q4b

c $4 - 7x = 3(x - 10)$

2
Q4c

d Solve this inequality.

$3x - 2 > 4x - 3$

2
Q4d

5 Joanna is saving for her holidays. She saves £15 each week.

a How many weeks will it be before she has more than £250?

2
Q5a

Wendy and William are also saving for their holidays. Their father gives them £20 each.

b Wendy saves £4 a week. After n weeks she has a total of £P. Write a formula connecting P and n.

1
Q5b

c William's total after *n* weeks is given by the formula

$$T = 20 + \frac{n^2}{10}$$

After how many weeks will Wendy and William have the same amount?

....

....

6 **a** A rectangle is divided into three smaller rectangles and a square. The areas of three of the parts are shown on the diagram.
Find the area of the remaining rectangle.

95 cm²	25 cm²
228 cm²	

....

b Another rectangle has area 1200 cm².
Its width is one third of its length.
Use algebra to find its dimensions.

....

Max. 17
Qs 4–6
subtotal

7 Find the lettered angles. In each case give a reason for your answer.

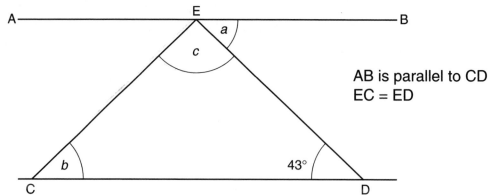

AB is parallel to CD
EC = ED

2
Q7a

2
Q7b

2
Q7c

a Angle *a* = ...° Reason ....

b Angle *b* = ...° Reason ....

c Angle *c* = ...° Reason ....

8 Mr Smith has a briefcase with a combination lock.
There are three wheels on the lock.
Each wheel has ten positions, numbered 0 to 9.

   a The numbers to open the lock are 3, 1, 2 but Mr Smith has forgotten the order.

   (i) List all the possible combinations.

2
Q8a(i)

....

   (ii) What is the probability that he will get it right first time?

1
Q8a(ii)

....

b To help him remember, he changes the numbers. The first is 1 and the other two add up to 7.

   (i) List all the possible combinations.

....

He remembers that no two digits are the same.

   (ii) What is the probability that he will get it right first time?

....

   (iii) What is the probability that he will get it right in three attempts?

....

9 Below are some fractions.

   a Arrange these fractions in size order, smallest first.

$$\frac{2}{3}, \frac{5}{8}, \frac{5}{6}, \frac{13}{24}$$ ....

   b Work these out. In each case write your answer as a fraction in its lowest terms.

    (i) $\dfrac{2}{3} + \dfrac{5}{8} =$ ....

    (ii) $\dfrac{2}{3} \times \dfrac{5}{8} =$ ....

Max. 19
Qs 7–9
subtotal

3
Q10

10 This trough is a prism with a trapezium as its cross section. The dimensions are in centimetres.

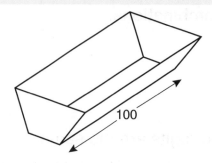 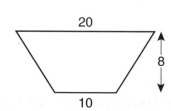

Calculate the volume.

....

....

1
Q11a

11 a John calculates the value of $\frac{0.137}{0.981}$ to be 0.134.

Without doing any calculation, explain how you know he is wrong.

....

1
Q11b(i)

1
Q11b(ii)

1
Q11b(iii)

1
Q11b(iv)

b $\sqrt{26} = 5.1$ $\sqrt{2.6} = 1.6$ to one decimal place.
Use these to find the following.

(i) $\sqrt{260}$ = ...

(ii) $\sqrt{0.26}$ = ...

(iii) $\sqrt{26\,000}$ = ...

(iv) $\sqrt{0.000\,26}$ = ...

12 Scientists have measured different breeds of penguin in the Antarctic.

Breed of penguin	Height (cm)	Mass (kg)
Emperor	114	29.5
King	94	15.9
Yellow-eyed	65	15.4
Fjordland	56	13.2
Southern Blue	40	11.0

a Draw a scatter graph for these data.

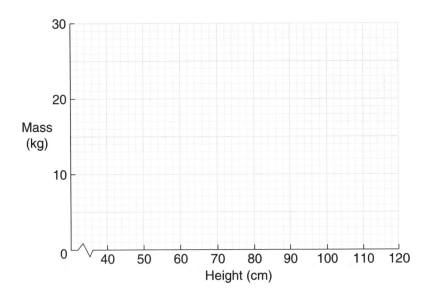

2

Q12a

b Describe the correlation.

....

1

Q12b

◆

c Another breed of penguin has a mass of 19 kg. Estimate its height. Say how you found it.

2

Q12c

Max. 13

Qs

10–12

subtotal

....

....

39

Test D
Levels 5–7

START

FINISH

CALCULATOR CAN BE USED

1 Here are some pictures of everyday objects.
Estimate the measurements.

.... cm   .... m

.... kg   .... g

2 The diagram shows a rhombus and the lengths of its diagonals.

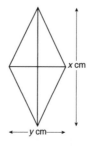

a (i) Explain why the area is given by the formula
$A = \frac{1}{2}xy$.

....

(ii) Find A when $x = 17$ and $y = 7$.

....

(iii) Find x when $A = 7.56$ and $y = 2.7$.

....

b (i) Write down the formula for the perimeter (P) of this rectangle.

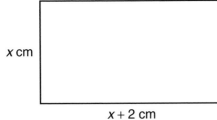

x cm

$x + 2$ cm

....

....

(ii) Find P when $x = 24$.

....

(iii) Find x when $P = 5$.

....

3 These pie charts show how land is used on two continents.

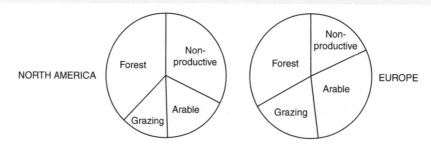

2
Q3a

a Make two comparisons between the land use on these continents.

....

....

1
Q3b

b Mark thinks there is more arable land in Europe than in North America. Explain why this may not be true.

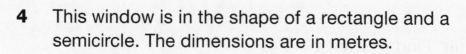

....

4 This window is in the shape of a rectangle and a semicircle. The dimensions are in metres.

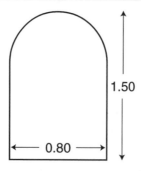

1.50

← 0.80 →

1
Q4a

a Change 1.50 m into centimetres.

....

b Change 0.80 m into millimetres.

1
Q4b

....

c Make an accurate drawing of the window. Use a scale of 1 cm to 20 cm.

◆

3
Q4c

d Find the perimeter of the window.

2
Q4d

....

e Find the area of the window.

3
Q4e

....

Max. 13
Qs 3–4
subtotal

5 A supermarket sells AMAZ washing powder in three sizes.

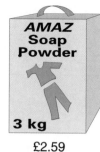

7.5 kg £6.59

3 kg £2.59

690 g 65p

Which is the best value? Show how you decide.

....

....

....

6 A photograph is enlarged to make a poster.
The widths and heights are shown in centimetres.

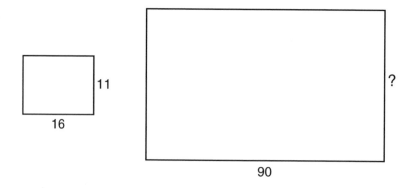

11

16

?

90

a How high is the poster?

....

44

b The photograph was enlarged from a negative.
The height of the negative is 24 mm.

How wide is the negative?

2
Q6b

....

7 Look at these scatter diagrams.

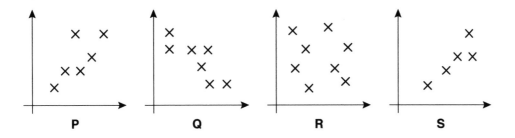

P   Q   R   S

a Describe the correlation in diagram S.

◆

1
Q7a

....

b Describe the correlation in diagram Q.

◆

1
Q7b

....

c Some students took both the Mathematics papers in
the Key Stage 3 Test.

Which diagram could show their results?

◆

1
Q7c

1
Q7d

....

d Which diagram could show the value of a second-
hand car plotted against its age?

Max. 12
Qs 5–7
subtotal

45

....

2
Q8

8 The temperature C in °Celsius is connected to the temperature F in °Fahrenheit by the formula

$$C = \frac{5}{9}(F - 32)$$

Find the temperature that has the same value in °C as °F.

....

9 The fastest ever drive from the bottom of South America to the top of North America – a distance of 23 720 km – took 24 days.

a Calculate the average speed in km/h for this journey.

2
Q9a

....

3
Q9b

b Estimate how long it would take to walk the same distance. Show all your workings and assumptions clearly.

....

....

....

10 The table shows the ages of 120 people living in a block of flats.

Age	Frequency
Up to 10	17
10 and up to 20	7
20 and up to 30	37
30 and up to 40	13
40 and up to 50	8
50 and up to 60	12
60 and up to 70	26

a Calculate an estimate of the mean age.

3
Q10a

b Estimate the median age. Show how you found it.

2
Q10b

c The people in another block of flats have a mean age of 35 and a median age of 35.

Compare the two age distributions.

2
Q10c

3
Q11

◆

11 The distances marked on the sides of this triangle are in metres.
Find its area.

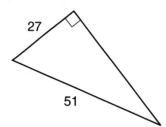

27

51

12 a Solve the following equations.

(i) $4x - 3(x - 2) = 0$

2
Q12a(i)

(ii) $\frac{1}{2}(3 - x) = x + 2$

2
Q12a(ii)

b Solve these simultaneous equations.

3
Q12b

$3x + 4y = 7$

$x - 2y = -6$

Max. 10
Qs
11–12
subtotal

48

MARKS

WITHOUT CALCULATOR

1 Pat wants to make a scale model of a tent.
She uses a scale where 8 cm represents 5 feet.

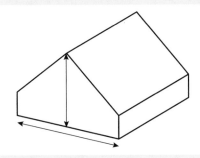

a The width of the tent is 8 feet.
What is the width of the model?

2
Q1a

b The height of the model is 5 cm.
What is the height of the real tent?

2
Q1b

2 The mean weight of 10 men is 75 kg.
The mean weight of 15 women is 50 kg.

What is the mean weight of all 25 people?

3
Q2

1
Q3a

3 Estimate the values of these expressions. Show
your working.

1
Q3b

a $\dfrac{64.7 \times 18.3}{27.4}$

Max. 9
Qs 1–3
subtotal

b $\dfrac{0.73 \times 56.2}{18.7 - 7.9}$

49

4   Jenny has two dogs, Rover and Tiny.
Rover eats $\frac{3}{5}$ of a tin of food each day.

a How many tins will Rover need for a week?

....

The dogs also have some biscuits.
Between them, they eat 600 g a day.
This is divided in the ratio Rover:Tiny = 3:1.

b How much biscuit does Rover eat in a day?

....

Tiny eats $\frac{1}{4}$ of a tin of food a day.

c Work out what fraction of a tin Rover and Tiny eat between them each day.

....

5   Dillon and Karl are testing six-sided dice. They decide Dillon's dice is fair.

a What is the probability that Dillon will throw a 6 next time?

....

Karl's dice is biased. He works out these probabilities.

Number on dice	1	2	3	4	5	6
Probability	0.2	0.1	0.1		0.2	0.1

b Work out the probability that Karl throws a 4.

....

c They both throw their dice.
   (i) Find the probability that they both throw a 6.

....

   (ii) Find the probability that one of them throws a 6.

....

6 Look at this grid.

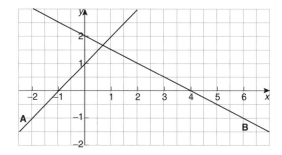

a Draw the line with equation $y = x - 1$. Label it **C**.

b Find the equation of line **B**.

....

c Use the graphs to solve the simultaneous equations:

$$x - y = -1$$
$$x + 2y = 4$$

....

Max. 17
Qs 4–6
subtotal

51

$\dfrac{1}{Q7a}$

$\dfrac{3}{Q7b}$ ◆

7 *n* is an integer.

a Explain why $2n - 1$ is an odd number.

....

b Multiply two consecutive odd numbers. Add 1 to the result. Prove that this is a multiple of 4.

....

....

8 Two goats live in this small field.

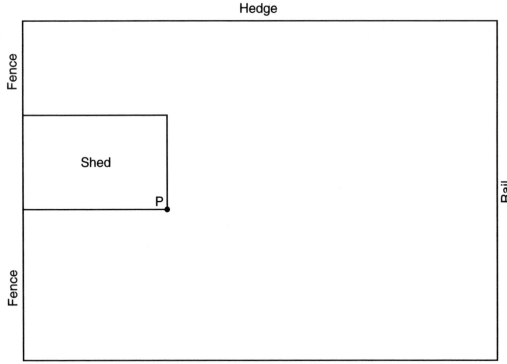

Hedge

Fence

Fence

Shed

P

Rail

Hedge   *Scale: 1 cm represents 1 m*

Nanny is fastened to the rail.

Her rope is 5 metres long. The end fastened to the rail can slide along the rail from one side of the field to the other.

a Mark accurately on the diagram where Nanny can go.

Billy is also tied to a 5 m rope.

The other end of his rope is fastened to the corner of the shed at P.

b Mark accurately on the diagram where Billy can go.

c Show clearly where they both can go.

9 Multiply out the brackets and simplify the following:

a $3(x - 2) + 4(2x - 3)$

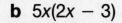

....

b $5x(2x - 3)$

....

c $x(2x + 5) - 3x(x - 2)$

....

Max. 13
Qs 7–9
subtotal

10 Complete the questions below, showing your answers on this diagram.

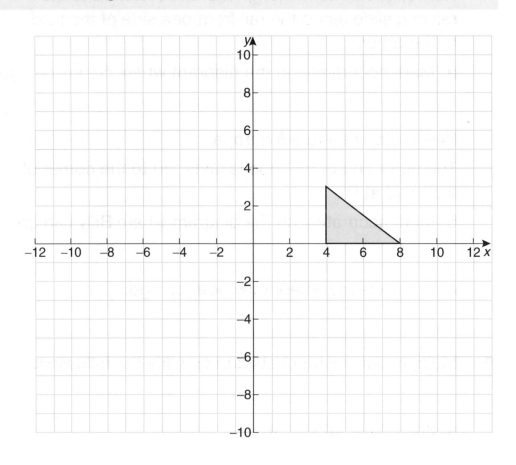

a Rotate the shaded triangle about the origin through 90° anticlockwise. Label it A.

b Reflect the shaded triangle in $x = -1$. Label it B.

c Enlarge the shaded triangle with centre the origin and scale factor $\frac{1}{2}$. Label it C.

11 The cumulative frequency graphs show how long electric lamps lasted. There are samples from two different makes, **A** and **B**.

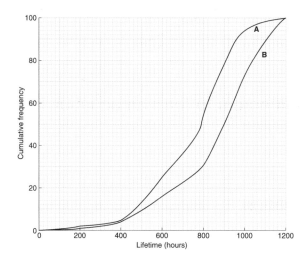

a How many lamps are there in each sample?

....

b For sample **A**, find:

(i) the median

....

(ii) the interquartile range

....

(iii) how many lamps were still working after 900 hours

....

c Which lamp would you buy? Give a reason.

A ☐   B ☐

....

1
Q11a

1
Q11b(i)

2
Q11b(ii)

1
Q11b(iii)

1
Q11c

Max. 12
Qs 10–11
subtotal

55

12 Look at this right-angled triangle.

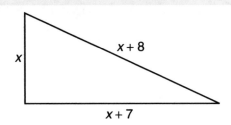

x

$x + 8$

$x + 7$

1
Q12a

a Use Pythagoras' theorem to form an equation in x.

....

2
Q12b

b Simplify your equation.

....

2
Q12c

c Solve the equation.

....

4
Q13

13 In triangle ABC, F is the midpoint of AB. FE is parallel to BC. DE is parallel to BA.
Prove that triangles AFE and EDC are congruent.

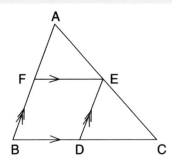

A

F   E

B   D   C

....

Max. 9
Qs
12–13
subtotal

56

Ask a friend or a parent to detach page 59 and read the questions for Test 1 to you. Each question will be read twice and you will then have a short time to complete your answer. For questions 1 to 6 it will be 5 seconds, for questions 7 to 20 you will have 10 seconds and for questions 21 to 30, 15 seconds. Any data you require is contained in the blue-tinted box. **You only need a pen or pencil. You must not use a calculator, ruler or any other geometrical instruments.**

Write your answers on the lines below.

1 .... 18 37

2 ....

3 .... ml

4 ....

5 .... 11:15 12:30

6 .... $2x = 36$

7 .... $5x - 5y$

8 .... $247 \div 0.43$

9 30 mm 30 cm
30 m 30 km
30 g 30 kg

10 .... $\frac{1}{2}x = 4$

11 .... m 12.5 5

12 .... 0.2

13 .... 2% 1000

14 ....

15 4349

16 .... $x^2 - x = 0$

17 ....° 65° 37°

18 .... 5 10 11

19 .... $2\frac{1}{2}$ 80

20 30 g 300 g
3000 g 30 kg
300 kg 3000 kg

21 .... 25 21 28 17 32

22 ....km/h 210 $1\frac{3}{4}$

23 .... $\frac{2}{5} + \frac{1}{3}$

24 30

25 £ ....

26 .... 0.2 0.1

27 .... 30 120

28 ....

29 .... $703 \div 19 = 37$

30 .... 0.85

Mental Mathematics Test 2:
Answer sheet

Ask a friend or a parent to detach page 60 and read the questions for Test 2 to you. Each question will be read twice and you will then have a short time to complete your answer. For questions 1 to 6 it will be 5 seconds, for questions 7 to 20 you will have 10 seconds and for questions 21 to 30, 15 seconds. Any data you require is contained in the blue-tinted box. **You only need a pen or pencil. You must not use a calculator, ruler or any other geometrical instruments.**

Write your answers on the lines below.

1		17	$\frac{35}{210}$
2	3.7 1.9	18	$x < -10$
3 ....cm	$7\frac{1}{2}$	19 ....cm	
4		20 ....%	£5 £4
5		21 ....cm^2	
6	0.065		3 cm / 5 cm / 4 cm
7	3.017	22	7 15 0
8			12 6
9 ....hours	100 50	23	$83 \times 41 = 3403$
10	$5x - 3$		10 209
11	14, 9, 4, ...	24 .... m	75 m^2
12	10 g 1 kg	25 .... °	110° 73° 90°
13	2:3	26	$\frac{3}{10} \times \frac{2}{15}$
14	0.05	27	3^2 2^3
15	150% 30	28	$29^3 = 24\ 389$
16	1 min 35 s 5 min 3 s, 52 s	29 .... s	3 8
		30	

Mental Mathematics Test 1:
Questions

INSTRUCTIONS

Detach this page from the book.

Read each question, exactly as printed, twice.

Allow a short time for each answer to be written down (on page 57).

For questions 1 to 6 allow 5 seconds, for questions 7 to 20 allow 10 seconds and for questions 21 to 30 allow 15 seconds.

1 Subtract eighteen from thirty-seven.

2 What number, divided by seven, gives eight?

3 How many millilitres are there in two and a half litres?

4 What is one hundred squared?

5 How many minutes is it from eleven fifteen to twelve thirty?

6 Two x equals thirty-six. What is x?

7 x minus y is three. What is five x minus five y?

8 What is the approximate value of the expression on your answer sheet?

9 Circle the measurement that is about the same as one foot.

10 Solve the equation on the answer sheet.

11 A tree trunk is twelve point five metres long. It is cut into five equal pieces. How long is each?

12 Work out nought point two squared.

13 What is two percent of one thousand?

14 What is the probability that a fair coin will land heads three times in a row?

15 Write the number four thousand, three hundred and forty-nine correct to two significant figures.

16 Solve the equation on your answer sheet.

17 Two angles of a triangle are sixty-five degrees and thirty-seven degrees. What is the third angle?

18 The mean of five numbers is ten. Another number is included. The new mean is eleven. What is the other number?

19 A bottle of milk will fill two and a half glasses. How many bottles are needed to fill eighty glasses?

20 Circle the mass that could be that of a holiday suitcase.

21 Find the median of the numbers on your answer sheet.

22 A car travelled two hundred and ten kilometres in one and three-quarter hours. What was its average speed?

23 Add the fractions on your answer sheet.

24 The pie chart shows how thirty students came to school. About how many walked?

25 A block of precious metal measures five by four by two centimetres. It costs one hundred pounds a cubic centimetre. How much is the block worth?

26 Work out nought point two divided by nought point one.

27 What is thirty as a percentage of one hundred and twenty?

28 What is the length of the third side of the triangle on your answer sheet?

29 Seven hundred and three divided by nineteen is thirty-seven. What is three point seven times nineteen?

30 Write down a fraction equal to nought point eight five.

Mental Mathematics Test 2:
Questions

1   Divide ten by five and then add two.

2   Work out three point seven minus one point nine.

3   How many centimetres are there in seven and a half metres?

4   Divide seventy-two by eight.

5   Multiply two by three by five by seven.

6   What number is one hundred times bigger than nought point nought six five?

7   Write the number three point nought one seven correct to two decimal places.

8   How many edges has a cube?

9   A car travelling at one hundred kilometres an hour completes a journey in x hours. How long will it take to complete the journey at fifty kilometres an hour.

10 What is the value of five x minus three when x equals two?

11 Write down the next number in the sequence fourteen, nine, four, …

12 What is ten grams as a fraction of a kilogram?

13 The ratio of apples to oranges in a fruit bowl is two to three. There are six apples. How many oranges are there?

14 The probability that my train will be late is nought point nought five. What is the probability that it will be on time?

15 Find one hundred and fifty percent of thirty.

16 I made three telephone calls lasting one minute thirty-five seconds, five minutes and three seconds and fifty-two seconds. What was the total time?

17 Write the fraction on the answer sheet in its lowest terms.

18 Write down a value of x which satisfies the inequality on your answer sheet.

19 Estimate the length of the line on your answer sheet.

20 The price of a ticket falls from £5 to £4. What percentage reduction is this?

21 Work out the area of the triangle on your answer sheet.

22 The answer sheet shows the number of points scored by a rugby player in five matches. Find the mean number of points.

23 Use the calculation on your answer sheet to work out how many forty-ones there are in ten thousand two hundred and nine.

24 A circular pond has area seventy-five square metres. Roughly what is its diameter?

25 Three angles of a quadrilateral are one hundred and ten, seventy-three and ninety. What is the fourth angle?

26 Multiply the fractions on your answer sheet.

27 Add together three to the power two and two to the power three.

28 Use the calculation on your answer sheet to work out the value of nought point two nine cubed.

29 Divide three minutes into eight equal parts. How many seconds in each?

30 A pilot steers a ship so that the distances from two marker buoys remain equal. Describe the ship's course.

Answers

HOW TO MARK THE TESTS

When marking the tests remember that the answers given are sample answers. You must look at your answers and judge whether they deserve credit. If they do, then award the mark. Although you should always try to spell words accurately, do not mark any answer wrong because the words are misspelt.

In these answers, the calculation is often given as well as the answer. Sometimes the method earns credit (e.g. Question 10b in Test B), but other times only the answer itself earns credit (e.g. Question 5a in Test A). In the latter cases, the working out has been provided to help you understand how to arrive at the correct answer.

When you go through the answers, try to work out where you have gone wrong. Make a note of the key points, so that you will remember them next time.

Only count the marks you scored in one hour on each test. Enter your marks for each test on the Marking grid on page 79, and then work out your level of achievement in these tests on page 78.

Test A Pages 12–21

1	**a**	multiple	*1 mark*
	b	square	*1 mark*
	c	factor	*1 mark*

TOTAL 3 MARKS

Make sure you do not confuse multiple and factor.

2 a   **b**   **c**   **d**

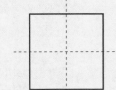  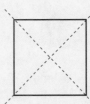

1 mark each: 4 marks

TOTAL 4 MARKS

There must be no extra lines drawn!

3

c   b   a   d
0   0.5   1

1 mark each: 4 marks

TOTAL 4 MARKS

4 Shape (c) is similar to the shaded shape.   *1 mark*
    Shape (d) is congruent to the shaded shape.   *1 mark*

TOTAL 2 MARKS

Examiner's tip

Remember, 'similar' means same shape, different size; 'congruent' means exactly the same shape and size.

5 a   43   *1 mark*
   b $F = 2A + 9$ *1 mark*
   c   14   *1 mark*

TOTAL 3 MARKS

Examiner's tip

Don't forget the '$F =$ ' is an important part of the formula and should not be left out.

6 a   430   *1 mark*
   b   62   *1 mark*
   c   70   *1 mark*
   d   100   *1 mark*
   e   1000   *1 mark*
   f   9.4   *1 mark*
   g   100   *1 mark*
   h   380   *1 mark*

TOTAL 8 MARKS

Examiner's tip

Remember that a number moves to the left one space every time you multiply by 10, and one to the right when you divide by 10.

7 a (i)   650 mm, 1070 mm   *1 mark*
    (ii)   0.65 m, 1.07 m   *1 mark*
   b   2 feet   *1 mark*
              $3\frac{1}{2}$ feet   *1 mark*

TOTAL 4 MARKS

Examiner's tip

You are expected to know that 1 foot is about 30 cm.

8	Brand B	1 mark
	Although it has a lower mean, it has a much narrower range	1 mark

TOTAL 2 MARKS

Although Brand A lasts longer on average, some of them will not last as long as those in Brand B. Brand B is more reliable/consistent. If you bought a lot of batteries, Brand A would be better.

9 a	£7.65	2 marks
b	£6.12	2 marks

TOTAL 4 MARKS

In each part there will be one mark for a correct method, e.g.

$$\begin{array}{r} 45 \\ \times 17 \\ \hline 450 \\ 315 \end{array}$$

and multiplying by 0.8 for part **b**.

10 a	$c + 7d$	1 mark
b	$2x - 4y$	1 mark
c	$15 - (-2)(-4) = 15 - 8$	1 mark
	$= 7$	1 mark
d (i)	$x = 30$	1 mark
(ii)	$3x = -3$	1 mark
	$x = -1$	1 mark

TOTAL 7 MARKS

In part **d(i)** you should not be tempted to divide both sides by 3.

11	$558 + 42 = 600$	2 marks

TOTAL 2 MARKS

Award 2 marks if all correct. Award 1 mark if the digits in the units column add up to 10.

12 a (i) $\frac{1}{5}$ or 0.2 or 20%   *1 mark*

     (ii) $\frac{3}{5}$ or 0.6 or 60%   *1 mark*

   b (i)   Too few results to be reliable   *1 mark*
     (ii) $\frac{23}{100}$ or 0.23 or 23%   *1 mark*

   c (i)   0.25   *1 mark*
    (ii)   0.75   *1 mark*

                                                              TOTAL 6 MARKS

 *Examiner's tip*
These answers show the only acceptable ways of writing probabilities. The answers to part **c** are found by subtracting from 1.

13 a   £300, £450   *1 + 1 marks*
   b   25%   *1 mark*

                                                              TOTAL 3 MARKS

 *Examiner's tip*
In part **a**, if you did not get the answers right, you will score 1 mark for using either two or three fifths. In part **b**, dividing 150 by 600 will earn 1 mark.

14 a   View 2   *1 mark*
   b   *3 marks*

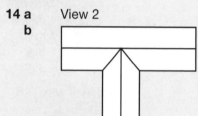

                                                              TOTAL 4 MARKS

 *Examiner's tip*
In part **b**, there could be one mark for the correct shape of the outline, one mark for the rooftops and one mark for the joins of the roofs.

15 a   25%   *1 mark*
   b   125 (people)   *1 mark*
   c   Not correct because although percentages are similar, the number of
        people interviewed is not the same   *1 mark*
   d   The same percentage of people surveyed in both towns   *1 mark*

                                                              TOTAL 4 MARKS

 *Examiner's tip*
The wording in part **c** can be different but the argument/reason must mention the different sample sizes.

                                                             TEST TOTAL 60 MARKS

1 **a** 5   **b** 6
    c 2   **d** 4

1 mark for each answer: 4 marks

TOTAL 4 MARKS

To find the order of rotational symmetry, count how many times the object fits on itself as you turn it. Don't forget to include the original position.

2 **a**   £2.70   *1 mark*
    b   62   *1 mark*
    c   £3.58   *1 mark*
    d $\frac{1}{3}$ *1 mark*
    e   50%   *1 mark*
    f $9 \times 15 + 4 \times 62 = 383$
        £3.83   *1 mark*

TOTAL 6 MARKS

It is easier to use the differences between the rates to find how much is saved in part **f**.

3 **a**   152.5   *1 mark*
    b   Frequency: 6, 6, 10, 5, 3   *2 marks*
    c   Bar graph (bars across 130−140, 140−150, etc.) or a polygon
        (points at 135, 145, etc.)   *1 mark*
        Heights plotted the same as your answer to part **b**   *1 mark*
    d   150 to 159   *1 mark*
    e   Ranjit's class has a higher modal group.   *1 mark*
        The shortest pupils are in Ranjit's class *or* the tallest are in the other class.   *1 mark*

TOTAL 8 MARKS

As there are an even number of heights, the median is between the middle two, 152 and 153. Your comparisons in part **e** should be about the heights, not the shape of the graph.

4 **a**   **b**   **c**

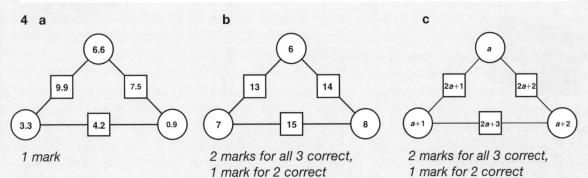

1 mark   *2 marks for all 3 correct,*   *2 marks for all 3 correct,*
             1 mark for 2 correct   *1 mark for 2 correct*

TOTAL 5 MARKS

Check by adding your answers in the circles at the end of each line.

Test B: Answers

5 a Three angles and two sides accurately drawn   *4 marks*
**   b** Angle = 66°   *1 mark*
      Other sides = 7.9 and 5.4 cm (or 79 and 54 m, full size) *1 mark*

TOTAL 6 MARKS

 Ask someone to check the accuracy of your drawing. The angles should be within 1° and the lengths within 1 mm of the stated sizes. If you have drawn it accurately, you should get these other measurements, to the same accuracy.

6 a (i) Straight line passing through (0, 1) and (4, 9)   *1 + 1 marks*
**   (ii)** Straight line passing through (0, 3) and (3, 0)   *1 + 1 marks*
**   b**   (0.7, 2.3)   *1 mark*

TOTAL 5 MARKS

 Your lines should be ruled carefully and reach at least as far as the points indicated. If drawn accurately the lines will meet at the given point, reading to the nearest 0.1.

7 a £7560   *1 mark*
**   b** 2940 litres   *1 mark*
**   c** £1996.26   *1 mark*
**   d** 20 000 × 0.1 × 1 = 2000   *2 marks*

TOTAL 5 MARKS

 There are other possible answers to part **d**. Make the numbers as simple as possible but without moving too far from the original size. One way to do this is shown. Since 0.14 is multiplied by 0.679, making one smaller and the other larger keeps the result about right. You will score one mark for an attempt to round the numbers, e.g. 21 000 × 0.15 × 0.68 – but not easy to work out in the head!

8 1000 ÷ 230 = 4.35   *1 mark*
     5 amp   *1 mark*

TOTAL 2 MARKS

 Show the result of your calculation as well as the size of the fuse.

9 a Rhombus   *1 mark*
**   b** Rectangle   *1 mark*
**   c** Trapezium   *1 mark*
**   d** Kite (or arrowhead)   *1 mark*

TOTAL 4 MARKS

 Apart from part **d**, there is only one answer in each case. An arrowhead is not a convex polygon but it has the same properties as a kite.

66

10 a $x = 3$ *1 mark*

b $2x = -12$ *1 mark*

     $x = -6$ *1 mark*

c $3 = 3x$ or $-3x = -3$ *1 mark*

     $x = 1$ *1 mark*

TOTAL 5 MARKS

 *Examiner's tip*

The correct solutions will earn both marks in parts **b** and **c**. However, it is a good idea to write down all the steps in the solution to equations, in case you make a mistake.

11 a 11 (millimetres)   *1 mark*

b 0 (millimetres)   *1 mark*

c 1.5 (millimetres)   *2 marks*

d 2.8 (millimetres)   *1 mark*

e Median – e.g. because it ignores the high value

    or Mean – e.g. because it gives a good indication of the amount of rain   *1 mark*

TOTAL 6 MARKS

 *Examiner's tip*

In **e** the mode is not a good average to use as only 4 days had no rain. Either median or mean with a valid reason would gain the mark.

12 a £70   *2 marks*

b 28.6%   *2 marks*

TOTAL 4 MARKS

 *Examiner's tip*

In each part there is a mark for the method if you got the answer wrong, e.g. $50 + \frac{2}{5} \times 50$ and $\frac{20}{70} \times 100$. Remember to use the price before the sale in part **b**.

TEST TOTAL 60 MARKS

Test C Pages 32–39

1 a Four axes   *1 mark*

    Order 4   *1 mark*

b Two axes   *1 mark*

    Order 2   *1 mark*

c Rhombus

1 mark

TOTAL 5 MARKS

 *Examiner's tip*

The shape in part **c** does not have to be a quadrilateral, as the answer to part **b** shows!

Test C: Answers

2 a   17   *1 mark*
  b   6.3   *1 mark*

TOTAL 2 MARKS

In part **b**, 13 must be added to the 50 before dividing by 10.

3 a $2\,|\,5$ means 25   *1 mark*

0	6										0	6							
1	6	7	3	9	3	9	6	0			1	0	3	3	6	6	7	9	9
2	5	3	6	0	4	0	7	5	4	9	2	0	0	3	4	4	5	5	6	7	9
3	2	3	8	9	2						3	2	2	3	8	9			
4	8										4	8							

                                                                  2 marks

  b   Median = 24   *1 mark*

TOTAL 4 MARKS

The stem-and-leaf diagram for part **a** should be ordered (as above right). The diagram above left is a working diagram, but you can still score both marks even if you don't use a working diagram.

The median in part **b** is the 13th number in the ordered stem-and-leaf diagram.

4 a $x = 2\frac{1}{2}$ *1 mark*
  b $2x + 6 = 5$ or $x + 3 = 2\frac{1}{2}$ *1 mark*

     $x = -\frac{1}{2}$ *1 mark*
  c $4 - 7x = 3x - 30$ *1 mark*
     $x = 3.4$ *1 mark*
  d $-x > -1$ or $1 > x$ *1 mark*
     $x < 1$ *1 mark*

TOTAL 7 MARKS

Great care is needed with the negative signs in part **d**. $1 > x$ is a satisfactory solution but it is usual to finish with x on the left.

5 a   17   *2 marks*
  b $P = 4n + 20$ *1 mark*
  c $4n + 20 = 20 + \frac{n^2}{10}$ *1 mark*

     $n = 40$ *1 mark*

TOTAL 5 MARKS

Remember to show the method in part **a**. The answer is not 16 as she will not have reached £250 by then, only £240. There is another solution in part **c**, $n = 0$ (they both start with £20).

68

6 a   Finding width and height of rectangle (5 cm and 19 cm)   *1 mark*
         60 cm^2 *1 mark*
b $3x^2 = 1200$ *1 mark*
         $x^2 = 400$ *1 mark*
         20 and 60   *1 mark*

TOTAL 5 MARKS

Examiner's tip   The starting point in part **a** must be the square. Other ways involve guessing.

7 a   43°   *1 mark*
         alternate angles between AB and CD   *1 mark*
b   43°   *1 mark*
         isosceles triangle ECD   *1 mark*
c   94°   *1 mark*
         angles of a triangle add up to 180°   *1 mark*

TOTAL 6 MARKS

Examiner's tip   Don't be tempted to measure the angles on the test paper, as they are far from accurate! Use the information given. Alternate angles between parallel lines are sometimes called Z angles.

8 a (i)   123, 132, 213, 231, 312, 321   *2 marks*
     (ii) $\frac{1}{6}$ *1 mark*
   b (i)   107, 170, 116, 161, 125, 152, 134, 143   *2 marks*
     (ii) $\frac{1}{6}$ *1 mark*
     (iii) $\frac{3}{6}$ or $\frac{1}{2}$ *1 mark*

TOTAL 7 MARKS

Examiner's tip   You may make one error and still score one mark in each of parts **a(i)** and **b(i)**. Be systematic in writing them down as this will help you not to miss one or repeat one, both of which will lose a mark. In part **b(ii)**, two combinations have one repeated so are not included when calculating the probability.

9 a $\frac{13}{24}$, $\frac{5}{8}\left(=\frac{15}{24}\right)$, $\frac{2}{3}\left(=\frac{16}{24}\right)$, $\frac{5}{6}\left(=\frac{20}{24}\right)$ *1 mark for correct equivalent fractions, 1 mark for correct order*   *2 marks*

   b (i) $\frac{16}{24} + \frac{15}{24} =$ *1 mark*

         $\frac{31}{24}$ or $1\frac{7}{24}$ *1 mark*

     (ii) $\frac{2 \times 5}{3 \times 8} = \frac{10}{24}$ *1 mark*

         $= \frac{5}{12}$ *1*

TOTAL 6 MARKS

Examiner's tip   The methods for combining fractions are shown above and earn marks.

Test C: Answers

10 Area of trapezium = 120 cm²   *1 mark*
       Volume = 120 × 100 = 12 000 cm³   *1 + 1 marks*

TOTAL 3 MARKS

Use the formulae given on page 8 for the area of the trapezium and the volume of the prism.

11 a Dividing by a number less than 1 increases the size of a number   *1 mark*
  b (i) 16   *1 mark*
   (ii) 0.51   *1 mark*
   (iii) 160   *1 mark*
   (iv) 0.016   *1 mark*

TOTAL 5 MARKS

Notice that the square root of a number less than 1 is larger than the original number.

12 a Scatter graph plotted   *2 marks*

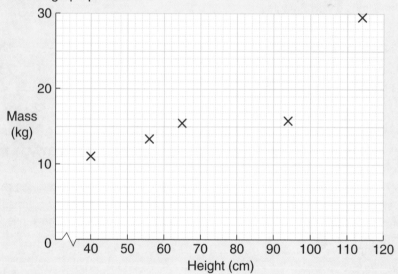

  b Positive   *1 mark*
  c Between 80 and 100   *1 mark*
        Read from a line of best fit or from the nearest point   *1 mark*

TOTAL 5 MARKS

It is not a strong positive correlation. A line of best fit will tend to ignore the point for the King penguin. If you use this for part **c**, your answer should be near 80.

TEST TOTAL 60 MARKS

Test D Pages 40–48

1 15 to 30 cm 4 to 6 m   *1 + 1 marks*
    1 to 2 kg 8 to 15 g   *1 + 1 marks*

   TOTAL 4 MARKS

You can check these afterwards but be careful with the bus!

2 a (i) The rhombus is half a rectangle measuring x by y.   *1 mark*
   (ii) 59.5 cm²   *1 mark*
   (iii) 5.6   *1 mark*
   b (i) $x + x + 2 + x + x + 2$ *1 mark*
      $4x + 4$ or $4(x + 1)$ *1 mark*
   (ii) 100   *1 mark*
   (iii) 0.25 or $\frac{1}{4}$ *1 mark*

   TOTAL 7 MARKS

The simplified expression will earn both marks in part **b(i)**.

3 a Proportion of Forest and Grazing about the same   *1 mark*
   More Arable in Europe or more Non-productive in North America   *1 mark*
   b The total area of North America is not the same as the total area of Europe.   *1 mark*

   TOTAL 3 MARKS

You may have some different answers in part **a**. When asked to make two comparisons, look for what is the same and what is different.

4 a 150 cm   *1 mark*
   b 800 mm   *1 mark*
   c Accurate drawing: lengths 4 cm and 7.5 cm   *1 mark*
         right angles   *1 mark*
         semicircle radius 2 cm   *1 mark*
   d $\frac{1}{2} \times \pi \times 0.8$ for semicircle   *1 mark*

      5.06 m   *1 mark*
   e $\frac{1}{2} \times \pi \times 0.4^2$ *1 mark*

      0.8×1.5 *1 mark*
      1.45 m²   *1 mark*

   TOTAL 10 MARKS

The answers to parts **d** and **e** are given correct to three significant figures. You would not lose marks here for giving more figures but it would not be sensible from the measurements given in the question.

5 $6.59 \div 7.5 = 0.879$ *1 mark*
         $2.59 \div 3 = 0.863$ *1 mark*
         $0.65 \div 0.69 = 0.942$ *1 mark*
         The 3 kg box is best as it costs less per kilogram.   *1 mark*

TOTAL 4 MARKS

You could instead calculate how much washing powder you get for £1 or 1p. The largest number will then represent the best buy.

6 a $90 \div 16 \times 11$ *1 mark*
           61.875, or 61.9 or 62 cm   *1 mark*
  b $24 \times 16 \div 11$ *1 mark*
           34.9 or 35 mm   *1 mark*

TOTAL 4 MARKS

The data in the question is to the nearest centimetre/millimetre, so similar accuracy is sensible for the answers. Notice that it is not necessary to convert the millimetres into centimetres in part **b**, as this is a proportional calculation and gives an answer also in millimetres.

7 a   (Strong) positive correlation   *1 mark*
  b   Negative correlation   *1 mark*
  c   P (or possibly S)   *1 mark*
  d   Q   *1 mark*

TOTAL 4 MARKS

8   Put $F = C$ $9C = 5(C - 32)$ *1 mark*
                        $4C = -160$ $C = -40$ *1 mark*

TOTAL 2 MARKS

You could just as well put $C = F$ and solve for F. The result should be the same!

9 a $\dfrac{23\,720}{24 \times 24} = 41.18$ km/h   *2 marks*
  b   e.g. 'Average' walking speed is 6 km/h   *1 mark*
           Drive speed is approximately 42 km/h
           Ratio of speeds = 42:6 = 7:1
           Ratio of times = 1:7
           Therefore walking takes $7 \times 24 = 168$ days   *2 marks*

TOTAL 5 MARKS

In **b** the time would be a guide to the minimum. There is a range of possible assumptions. Examiners would give credit for sensible assumptions and a time between 160 and 240 days.

Test D: Answers

10 a	Using midpoints 5, 15, 25, 35, 45, 55, 65	*1 mark*
	Multiplying these by the frequencies, adding and dividing by 120	*1 mark*
	35.7 years	*1 mark*
b	29 or 30 years	*1 mark*
	Median between 60th and 61st, at top of group 20 to 30	*1 mark*
c	Second more evenly distributed, or fewer old people	*1 mark*
	Mean is almost the same	*1 mark*

TOTAL 7 MARKS

 *Examiner's tip* When the mean and the median are about the same size, the distribution is balanced and not weighted to an extreme. In the first case here, the 26 people over 60 caused the mean to be higher than the median.

11	$\sqrt{51^2 - 27^2}$	*1 mark*
	$\sqrt{1872} \times 27 \div 2$	*1 mark*
	584	*1 mark*

TOTAL 3 MARKS

 *Examiner's tip* In this question you have to recognise that the third side is needed to find the area and that Pythagoras' theorem is the way to find it. The correct answer would earn all 3 marks.

12 a (i)	$4x - 3x + 6 = 0$	*1 mark*
	$x = -6$	*1 mark*
(ii)	$3 - x = 2x + 4$	*1 mark*
	$3x = -1$	
	$x = -\frac{1}{3}$	*1 mark*
b	$3x + 4y = 7$	
	$2x - 4y = -12$ (multiplying second equation by 2)	*1 mark*
	$5x = -5$	
	$x = -1$	*1 mark*
	$-1 - 2y = -6$ (substituting for x)	
	$y = 2\frac{1}{2}$	*1 mark*

TOTAL 7 MARKS

 *Examiner's tip* You could do part **b** by multiplying the second equation by 3 and then subtracting. This would give $10y = 25$.

TEST TOTAL 60 MARKS

Test E: Pages 49–56

1 a	$8 \times \frac{8}{5}$ cm	*1 mark*
	$= 12.8$ cm	*1 mark*
b	$5 \times \frac{5}{8}$ feet	*1 mark*
	$= 3\frac{1}{8}$ or 3.125 feet	*1 mark*

TOTAL 4 MARKS

Not a very sensible scale! As a check, notice that it is 1.6 cm to one foot. That means that the number of centimetres on the model should be greater than the number of feet on the real tent.

2 Total weight of men = 750 kg
Total weight of women = 750 kg *1 mark*
$1500 \div 25$ *1 mark*
= 60 kg *1 mark*

TOTAL 3 MARKS

An alternative method is to calculate $\frac{2}{5} \times 75 + \frac{3}{5} \times 50$, i.e. as a proportion calculation.

3 a $\frac{60 \times 20}{30} = 40$ *1 mark*

b $\frac{0.7 \times 60}{10}$ or $\frac{0.8 \times 50}{10}$ *1 mark*
= 4

TOTAL 2 MARKS

Try to choose approximations that make the arithmetic easy. Only give one significant figure in your answer.

4 a $7 \times \frac{3}{5} = 4\frac{1}{5}$ *1 mark*
5 tins needed *1 mark*
b $\frac{3}{4} \times 600$ *1 mark*
= 450 g *1 mark*
c $\frac{3}{5} + \frac{1}{4} = \frac{12+5}{20}$ *1 mark*
= $\frac{17}{20}$ *1 mark*

TOTAL 6 MARKS

If you got any of these fractions wrong, you need some more practice!

5 a $\frac{1}{6}$ *1 mark*
b 0.3 *1 mark*
c (i) $\frac{1}{6} \times 0.1 = \frac{1}{60}$ *1 mark*
(ii) $\frac{1}{6} \times 0.9 + \frac{5}{6} \times 0.1$ *1+1 mark*
$\frac{9}{60} + \frac{5}{60} = \frac{14}{60} = \frac{7}{30}$ *1 mark*

TOTAL 6 MARKS

It is easier to work in fractions here. Notice that in part **c(ii)** there are two possibilities – Dillon gets a 6 but Karl does not and vice versa. As these are alternatives (and exclusive) the probabilities are added.

6 a

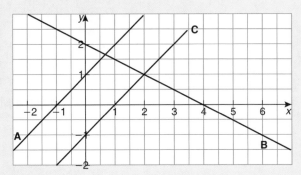

1 mark

b $x + 2y$ *1 mark*
   $= 4$ *1 mark*
c   Taking reading where A and B meet   *1 mark*
   $x = 0.7, y = 1.7$ *1 mark*

TOTAL 5 MARKS

Examiner's tip

If you wanted to (and you had time!), you could check your answer by algebra. This solution is $x = \frac{2}{3}, y = 1\frac{2}{3}$.

7 a $2n$ is even, as it is $2 \times$ an integer.
   1 less is the number before, which is odd.   *1 mark*
b   Consecutive odd numbers could be $2n - 1$ and $2n + 1$ *1 mark*
   $(2n - 1)(2n + 1) = 4n^2 - 1$ *1 mark*
   Add 1 to give $4n^2$, which is $4 \times$ an integer and therefore a multiple of 4.   *1 mark*

TOTAL 4 MARKS

Examiner's tip

Notice how the first part of the question gave you a start. To prove that something is true for all numbers, you must use a general case – here it is algebraic. It is no good trying some specific examples, even if they do all work. It does not prove it will work for others.

8

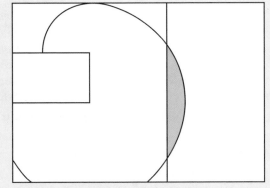

a   Straight line 5 cm from rail   *1 mark*
b   (Part) circle radius 5 cm   *1 mark*
   Quarter circle radius 2.5 cm   *1 mark*
c   Segment shaded blue   *1 mark*

TOTAL 4 MARKS

Examiner's tip

Ruler, compasses and sharp pencil are needed to answer this question. Don't obliterate your drawing with the shading.

9 a $3x - 6 + 8x - 12$ *1 mark*
       $= 11x - 18$ *1 mark*
  b $10x^2 - 15x$ *1 mark*
  c $2x^2 + 5x - 3x^2 + 6x$ *1 mark*
       $= -x^2 + 11x$ *1 mark*

TOTAL 5 MARKS

Be very careful with the negative signs.

10

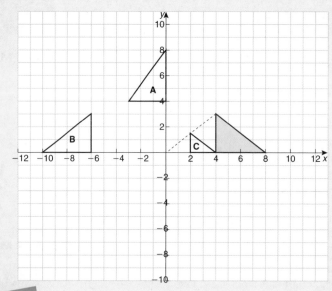

Two marks for each correct action: 6 marks
TOTAL 6 MARKS

There are two marks for each part. Any error will lose one mark.

11 a   100   *1 mark*
  b (i)   785 hours   *1 mark*
    (ii) $880 - 600$ *1 mark*
         280 hours   *1 mark*
   (iii) $100 - 78 = 22$ *1 mark*
  c   B, it has a longer average life (median 900 hours)   *1 mark*

TOTAL 6 MARKS

Even if you read one of the quartiles wrongly, you could get a mark for subtracting them. When giving your reason in part **c**, it is a good idea to include a statistic (in this case the median) to support what you say.

12 a $(x + 8)^2 = x^2 + (x + 7)^2$ *1 mark*
  b $x^2 - 2x$ *1 mark*
         $-15 = 0$ *1 mark*
  c $(x - 5)(x + 3) = 0$ *1 mark*
         $x = 5$ or $x = -3$ *1 mark*

TOTAL 5 MARKS

The solution of the equation gives two values for x, both of which you should have given. However, had you been asked to find the lengths of the sides of the triangle, $x = -3$ is not a possible value, so $x = 5$ gives the lengths 5, 12, 13.

Test E: Answers

13	ED = FB (opposite sides of a parallelogram)	*1 mark*
	FB = FA (given)	
	Angle AEF = Angle ECD	
	(corresponding angles, FE parallel to BC)	*1 mark*
	Angle DEC = Angle BAC	
	(corresponding angles DE parallel to BA)	*1 mark*
	Triangles congruent (AAS)	*1 mark*

TOTAL 4 MARKS

For this test of congruence to work, the equal sides must correspond, i.e. they must both be opposite equal angles.

TEST TOTAL 60 MARKS

Mental Mathematics Test: Answers

Mental Mathematics Test 1: Page 59

1	19	9	30 cm	17	78°	25	£4000
2	56	10	$x = 8$	18	16	26	2
3	2500	11	2.5	19	32	27	25%
4	10 000	12	0.04	20	30 kg	28	12
5	75	13	20	21	25	29	70.3
6	18	14	$\frac{1}{8}$ or 0.125	22	120	30	$\frac{85}{100}$ or $\frac{17}{20}$
7	15	15	4300	23	$\frac{11}{15}$		
8	600	16	$x = 1$ or 0	24	18		

Mental Mathematics Test 2: Page 60

1	4	10	7	18	e.g.	25	87°
2	1.8	11	−1		−11, −20, −10.1	26	$\frac{6}{150}$ or $\frac{1}{25}$
3	750	12	$\frac{1}{100}$	19	Between 2 and 3 cm	27	17
4	9	13	9			28	0.0243 89
5	210	14	0.95	20	20%	29	22.5 s
6	6.5	15	45	21	6 cm²	30	Perpendicular bisector of line joining buoys
7	3.02	16	7 minutes 30 seconds	22	8		
8	12			23	249		
9	2x hours	17	$\frac{1}{6}$	24	10 m		

You must listen carefully. 'Sixty' can sound like 'sixteen' if you are not concentrating. Ten seconds may not sound very long but, with practice, you should be able to answer questions like this in that time in your head. To get some more practice, ask someone to make up other questions like these, but with different numbers. Your score should soon improve – your target is to get them all right!

Determining your level

When you have marked a test, enter the total number of marks you scored for each question on the Marking grid overleaf. Then add them up and enter the test total on the grid.

Using the total for each test, look at the charts below to determine your level for each test.

Test A or Test B

Level 3 or below	Level 4	Level 5	Level 6
up to 13	14–26	27–39	40+

After you have worked out separate levels for Tests A and B and Mental Mathematics Test 1, add up your total marks for the three tests. Use this total and the chart below to determine your overall level for Maths at this point.

Total for Tests A and B and Mental Mathematics Test 1

Level 3 or below	Level 4	Level 5	Level 6
up to 31	32–63	64–94	95+

If your results from Tests A and B indicate that you are working at Level 4 or higher, you should try Tests C and D some time later. The chart below shows you how to find your level for each of Tests C and D.

Test C or Test D

Level 4 or below	Level 5	Level 6	Level 7 or above
up to 15	16–24	25–42	43+

If your results from Test C and D indicate that you are working at Level 6 or higher, you should try Test E. The chart below shows you how to find your level for Test E.

Test E

Level 5 or below	Level 6	Level 7	Level 8	Gifted & Talented
up to 13	14–24	25–41	42–50	51+

FINDING YOUR OVERALL LEVEL IN MATHS

After you have found your level for each test, add up your total marks for Tests C and D and Mental Mathematics Test 2. Use this total and the chart below to determine your overall level in Maths. The chart also shows you how your level compares with the target level for your age group.

Total for Tests C and D and Mental Mathematics Test 2

Level 4 or below	Level 5	Level 6	Level 7
up to 37	38–64	65–99	100+
Working towards target level	Working at target level for age group		Working beyond target level

Marking grid

Test A Pages 12–21

Question	Marks available	Marks scored	Question	Marks available	Marks scored	Question	Marks available	Marks scored
1	3	①	6	8		11	2	
2	4		7	4		12	6	
3	4		8	2		13	3	
4	2		9	4		14	4	
5	3		10	7		15	4	
						Total	60	

Test B Pages 22–31

Question	Marks available	Marks scored	Question	Marks available	Marks scored	Question	Marks available	Marks scored
1	4		5	6		9	4	
2	6		6	5		10	5	
3	8		7	5		11	6	
4	5		8	2		12	4	
						Total	60	

Test C Pages 32–39

Question	Marks available	Marks scored	Question	Marks available	Marks scored	Question	Marks available	Marks scored
1	5		5	5		9	6	
2	2		6	5		10	3	
3	4		7	6		11	5	
4	7		8	7		12	5	
						Total	60	

Test D Pages 40–48

Question	Marks available	Marks scored	Question	Marks available	Marks scored	Question	Marks available	Marks scored
1	4		5	4		9	5	
2	7		6	4		10	7	
3	3		7	4		11	3	
4	10		8	2		12	7	
						Total	60	

Test E Pages 49–56

Question	Marks available	Marks scored	Question	Marks available	Marks scored	Question	Marks available	Marks scored
1	4		6	5		11	6	
2	3		7	4		12	5	
3	2		8	4		13	4	
4	6		9	5				
5	6		10	6		Total	60	

	Marks available	Marks scored
Mental Mathematics Test 1 (p. 59)	30	
Mental Mathematics Test 2 (p. 60)	30	

National Curriculum
Key Stage 3 Age 13–14

Practice Papers

Key Stage 3
National Tests

SCIENCE

How the Key Stage 3 National Tests will affect your education

- All students in Year 9 (age 13–14) will take National Tests in English, Mathematics and Science. These important tests are held in May each year and are designed to be an objective assessment of the work you will have done during Key Stage 3 (Years 7–9) of the National Curriculum.

- You will also have your school work assessed by your teachers. These teacher assessments will be set alongside your results in the National Tests to give a clear picture of your overall achievement.

- In July, the test results together with the teacher assessments will be reported to parents/guardians.

- The results may be used by your teacher to help place you in the appropriate teaching group for some GCSE courses next year.

How this book will help your education

- This book offers plenty of practice in the type of question you will face in the Key Stage 3 National Test for Science.

- The answers and a mark scheme have been provided to allow you to check how you have done.

- The 'Examiner's tip' boxes in the Answers section give you advice on how to improve your answers and avoid common mistakes.

- A unique Marking grid allows you to record your results and estimate the level of the National Curriculum at which you are working.

KS3 Science Contents

What you need to know about the National Tests

What is the purpose of National Tests?

The tests, taken by students in Year 9, have several functions:

- they provide the government with a snapshot picture of attainment throughout the country, enabling it to make judgements about whether standards are improving nationally;
- they give information to OFSTED about schools' achievements, so that they can judge which schools are improving and which are deemed to be failing their students;
- they give you information about your progress compared to national standards;
- they may be used by teachers to place you in the appropriate teaching group for the GCSE courses starting in Year 10.

How do the tests work?

In May of Year 9, you will take tests on the core subjects of English, Mathematics and Science. In Science there are two tests. You will have one hour to complete each test. The tests are not marked in school by a teacher, but posted off to an external marker, who is often a teacher in another school or a retired teacher. External markers have been trained in marking the tests so that all students' test papers throughout the country are marked to the same standard.

Once the tests have been marked, the mark is translated into a 'level'. The level that each mark corresponds to is decided according to results gained in pre-tests and the tests themselves. It varies slightly from year to year. The test papers, marks and levels are returned to your school in July. The levels are then reported to your parents/guardians.

What do the tests assess?

The tests are designed to assess your knowledge, skills and understanding in the context of the programme of study set out in the National Curriculum. This can be found on the National Curriculum website, www.nc.uk.net. The programme of study is divided into four sections, called Attainment Targets:

- Sc1 – Scientific enquiry – ideas and evidence in science and investigative skills.
- Sc2 – Life processes and living things – animals and plants and their environments.
- Sc3 – Materials and their properties – grouping and changing materials and separating mixtures.
- Sc4 – Physical processes – forces, electricity, light and sound.

Questions in the tests cover all four Attainment Targets, but the questions about scientific enquiry (Sc1) are usually set within the context of one of the other Attainment Targets.

What are the levels and what do they mean?

There is a set of benchmark standards that measure a student's progress through the first three Key Stages of the National Curriculum. Attainment is measured in steps called 'levels', from 1 to 7. The National Curriculum document sets out the knowledge, skills and understanding that students should demonstrate at each level. The government target is for students to achieve level 2 at the end of Key Stage 1, level 4 at the end of Key Stage 2 and level 5 or 6 at the end of Key Stage 3. The chart below shows these government targets.

At the end of Key Stage 3, students take a test targeted at either level 3 to level 6 or level 5 to level 7. Pupils who achieve an exceptionally high mark, well above that needed for the top level, will be assessed as Gifted and Talented.

How does this book help me?

This book gives you practice in answering the type of question that you will face in the actual tests. By practising questions in this way, you will feel under less pressure and be more relaxed. Being relaxed helps students to perform at their best in tests, so we have targeted the questions at levels 4–7, allowing you to become familiar with most of the types of question that are asked in the tests.

The tests in this book are longer than the SAT tests to give you the widest range of possible questions. The actual SAT tests are each 1 hour long.

How you should progress

Exceeded targets for age group

Achieved targets for age group

Working towards targets for age group

Preparing and practising for the Science Test

The questions in this book test the same things as the actual test papers:

- knowledge
- understanding
- handling information
- interpreting information and data
- solving problems
- using experiments to test ideas.

What are the key features of this book?

This book contains all you need to prepare for the tests:

- National Curriculum requirements – key information for each of the Attainment Targets Sc1, Sc2, Sc3 and Sc4.
- Questions – two practice test papers targeted at levels 4–7.
- Answers – showing the responses that will gain credit in the tests and how the marks are allocated.
- Examiner's tips – advice as to how you can improve your performance.
- Level charts – what the marks mean in terms of National Curriculum levels.

How should I use this book?

Start by taking Test A. Before rushing into it, make sure that you have:

- read the instructions on page 11;
- a quiet, comfortable room in which to work, where you will not be disturbed;
- a pen, pencil, rubber and ruler.

Allow 75 minutes to take the test. You are allowed to ask an adult to explain the meaning of words you do not understand, provided that they are not scientific terms such as 'evaporation'.

After completing the test, work through the papers along with the answers and advice at the back of the book. It is a good idea to highlight or make a note of areas where you do not do well, so that you can revise these at a later stage. Record your marks in the top half of the boxes in the margin.

Work out the total marks gained for each question, write them in the grid on page 75 and add them up to arrive at the total mark for the paper. You can then use the charts on page 74 to determine the level of your performance on this test.

When you are ready, you should take Test B, using a similar procedure as with Test A. The marks and level that you achieve on this test will inform you about your progress and identify any remaining areas of weakness. These should be revised thoroughly.

You can often improve your understanding by writing down brief explanations of key concepts.

Questions marked with a diamond (♦) are testing aspects of Sc1.

What does the level mean?

The tests in this book give a guide as to the level that you are likely to achieve in the actual tests. We hope that, through practice, these tests will give you the confidence to achieve your best. By working through the answers and notes, you should be able to improve your achievement.

How do I prepare to take the actual tests?

You should revise the topics that you did not do very well on. The Letts **Key Stage 3 Success** range shown on the back cover is our recommended revision source.

A few days before the test:

- work through the questions in Tests A and B again and make sure that you understand the correct answers to each question;
- check that you know what test papers you will be taking and when these are to be sat;
- double check that you have the necessary equipment, including a spare pen and pencil.

Finally, try and avoid putting yourself under pressure. If you have prepared thoroughly for the tests, you can be confident that you will do your best.

National Curriculum requirements

The next few pages give you information about the knowledge required at each level for the Attainment Targets, plus some practice questions to help you focus.

Sc1 Scientific enquiry: Requirements at each level

Level 4 Decide on the best approach to answer a question. Plan and carry out a fair test after predicting the outcome, using secondary sources of information where appropriate. Use simple graphs and charts to present results and show patterns. Explain their results and suggest how the procedure could be improved.

Level 5 Describe how scientific explanations are due to a combination of creative thinking and experimental evidence. Select the most appropriate approach, sources of information and apparatus to answer a scientific question. Use a suitable degree of precision for observations and measurements, repeat these where appropriate and present results as line graphs. Draw conclusions that are consistent with the evidence. Explain conclusions and suggest how more reliable evidence could be obtained.

Level 6 Use scientific knowledge and understanding in the planning. Select and use sources of information effectively. Make enough observations and measurements for the task. Measure with precision, using instruments with fine-scale divisions. Choose scales for graphs that enable them to show data and features effectively. Identify measurements and observations that do not fit the main pattern shown. Draw conclusions and use scientific knowledge and understanding to explain them. Make suggestions about how experiments could be improved.

Level 7 Use scientific knowledge and understanding to decide on an appropriate approach to a problem. Identify the key factors including ones which cannot readily be controlled. Make systematic observations and measurements with precision, using a wide range of apparatus. Identify when measurements and observations need to be repeated in order to obtain reliable data. Represent data in graphs, using lines of best fit. Draw conclusions that are consistent with the evidence and explain these using scientific knowledge and understanding. Consider whether the data collected is sufficient for the conclusions drawn.

Sc2 Life processes and living things: Requirements at each level

Level 4 Identify the major organs and organ systems of the human body and of a plant. Use keys to identify and group living things. Use a food chain to describe a feeding relationship.

Level 5 Describe the functions of the organs of the human body and of a plant. Compare the life cycles of an animal and of a plant. Explain why different organisms are found in different habitats and why living things need to be classified.

Level 6 Describe the life process of animals and plants. Describe the difference in cell structure of plants and animals. Explain cases of variation and how the organisms in a habitat are affected by their environment.

Level 7 Link life processes to the associated organs. Explain the chemical processes of respiration and photosynthesis. Distinguish between inherited and environmental causes of variation. Explain how feeding relationships affect the size of populations in a habitat.

Quick questions

1 Which organ filters the blood? ....

2 Which waste products are excreted in breathing out? ....
....

3 What food chemical is important for growth and repair? ....

4 Which part of a cell contains the genes? ....

5 What type of cell has a cell wall? ....

6 What type of joint is the elbow? ....

7 Name the chemicals used in respiration. ....

....

8 Is eye colour determined by inheritance or the environment? *Inheritance*

....

9 How are root hairs adapted to their job?

....

10 Where are male sex cells produced? *In the egg cell* ....

Sc3 Materials and their properties: Requirements at each level

Level 4 Classify materials as solids, liquids and gases. Use scientific terms such as evaporation and condensation correctly. Describe ways of separating mixtures and make predictions about whether changes are reversible or not.

Level 5 Distinguish metals from other solids by recognising metallic properties. Recognise evaporation and condensation taking place in unusual contexts. Suggest methods for separating mixtures.

Level 6 Describe physical and chemical changes and how new materials are made. Describe the differences in the arrangements of particles in solids, liquids and gases. Use word equations to summarise chemical reactions.

Level 7 Explain changes of state using the particle model. Explain the differences between elements, compounds and mixtures and use chemical symbols and formulae. Use the reactivity series to make predictions about chemical reactions.

Quick questions

1 In which state are the particles of a substance the most widely spaced?

....

2 What is the name of the smallest particle of an element? ....

3 Which of the following is a compound?
carbon   carbon dioxide   oxygen   ....

4 What method can be used to separate the dyes in a paint?

....

5 Complete the word equation:
zinc + sulphuric acid $\rightarrow$ zinc sulphate + ...

6 Which is more reactive, iron or gold? ....

7 What is the pH of a neutral solution? ....

8 What name is given to a solution when no more solute will dissolve?

....

9 Is evaporation a physical or a chemical change? ....

10 What can be used to neutralise an alkali? ....

Sc4 Physical processes: Requirements at each level

Level 4 Explain the effect of a switch in a circuit and the formation of shadows. Describe the effects of magnetic and gravitational forces, and how the position of the Sun changes in the sky during a day.

Level 5 Explain how to change the current in a circuit and how to alter the pitch and loudness of a sound. Recognise when the forces on an object are balanced or unbalanced and describe how objects are seen. Use a model of the Solar System to explain the length of a day and a year.

Level 6 Explain the transfer of energy by sound, light and electricity and how light is refracted and dispersed. Explain the relative brightness of stars and planets and the different effects of forces in causing pressure and rotation.

Level 7 Calculate the size of physical quantities, using the correct units. Explain why objects appear different colours in different coloured light and the factors that determine the strength of an electromagnet.

Quick questions

1 What type of circuit has only one current path? ....

2 Is a voltmeter connected in series or in parallel with a component?
....

3 What is the unit of electric current? ....

4 What is the job of current in a circuit?
....

5 What is the name for the turning effect of a force? ....

6 What term describes the effect of a force in cutting and piercing?
....

7 Which gives out its own light, a star, a planet or a moon? ....

8 How long does it take for the Earth to turn once on its own axis?
....

9 Are the forces on a bicycle that is speeding up balanced or unbalanced?
....

10 How can the pitch of a sound be increased?
....

Instructions

Test A and Test B should each take 75 minutes. Enter your start and finish times in the box at the beginning of each Test. You are advised to take a 5 minute break after question 9 in each test.

Try to answer all the questions.

Read the questions carefully. Sometimes you will use your knowledge to answer the questions. At other times, the question will give you a situation you have not met before. When this is the case, you will be given all the information you need to answer the question.

If you think, after reading a question carefully, that you cannot answer it, leave it and come back to it later.

The questions you have to answer are given in orange boxes. For example:

> Explain what happens to the speed of the yacht when the sail is lowered.

Write your answers fully on the test papers in this book. The ✏ shows where you should answer the question. The lines or space given should give you some indication of what is expected.

Look at the number of marks for each part of a question. This is shown in a box in the margin, for example:

1
Q1a

If a question is worth one mark, often a single word or single point is needed. A question worth two marks would need two distinct points to be made. You are very unlikely to score two marks with a single word answer.

There is also a box showing the maximum number of marks for each section. You can write in your subtotal, so that you can see at a glance how you are doing.

Look carefully at the words you write, particularly scientific words. Read your answers carefully to yourself and make sure you have clearly expressed what you mean.

GOOD LUCK!

Test A
Levels 4–7

START	
FINISH	

1 Most of the Earth's energy comes from the Sun.

 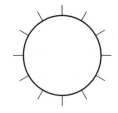

a How is energy transferred from the Sun to the Earth?

Q1a

..........Radiation..

b The diagram shows a modern wind turbine. Complete the sentence:

The turbine transfers ......wind........ energy from the wind to energy as ..Kenetic - electicity

2
Q1b

c A ball speeds up as it falls through the air.
What energy transfer takes place?

2
Q1c

..Gravitation potential energy..........

....

2 The diagram shows a daisy plant that grows in a lawn.
The lawn is cut each week in summer.

   a State two ways in which the daisy has adapted to
survive and reproduce in its environment.

2

Q2a

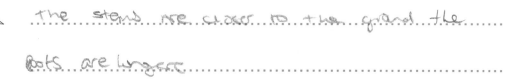

the stend are closs to the grand the

Rots are longer

   b The roots absorb substances from the soil.
How are the roots adapted to do this?

1

Q2b

They have large surface are.

   c Which **two** important substances do the roots absorb
from the soil?

2

Q2c

water & mineras

   d Explain why the cells that contain the most
chloroplasts are found in the leaves of the daisy.

2

Q2d

Max. 12

Qs 1–2

subtotal

13

3
Q3a

3 The diagram shows a human fetus in the womb.

  a Complete the table by using labels from the list below that match the letters on the diagram.

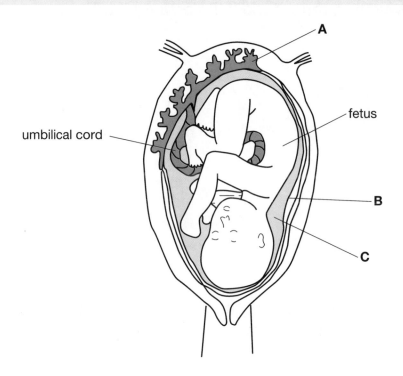

umbilical cord

A

fetus

B

C

amniotic fluid   amniotic sac   placenta   uterus

Letter	Label
A	
B	
C	

2
Q3b

  b What is the job of the umbilical cord?

  ....

  ....

  ....

c A new human life starts with fertilisation.
What happens in fertilisation?

1
Q3c

....

....

d Where does fertilisation normally take place?

1
Q3d

....

4 The table shows the times taken by some children to swim 80 metres in a race.

Swimmer	Time taken
Adam	27 seconds
Natalie	20 seconds
Kinglun	25 seconds
Claire	32 seconds
Faiza	29 seconds

a Who was the fastest swimmer?

1
Q4a

....

b Who came last?

1
Q4b

....

2
Q4c

c Work out Natalie's speed in m/s.

speed = ... m/s.

Max. 11
Qs 3–4
subtotal

5 Three circuits are shown in the diagram.

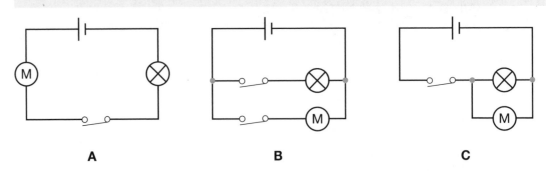

A   B   C

a Complete the following sentences.

(i) The lamp and the motor are connected in series
in circuit ....

1
Q5a(i)

(ii) The lamp and the motor must have the same current
in circuit ....

1
Q5a(ii)

(iii) The lamp and the motor are both worked by the
same switch in circuits .... and ....

1
Q5a(iii)

b What instrument would you use to measure the
current in circuit A?

1
Q5b

....

c The current that passes into the lamp in circuit B is
0.3A. How much current does the lamp use up?

1
Q5c

....

d Write down one way of increasing the current that
passes into the lamp in circuit B.

1
Q5d

....

6 The table gives some information about changes that occur when copper and three copper compounds are heated in air. In each case 1.0 g of the substance is heated.

Substance	Appearance before heating	Appearance after heating	Mass of solid residue
Copper	brown colour	black coating	1.1 g
Copper(II) carbonate	pale green powder	black powder	0.7 g
Copper(II) oxide	black powder	black powder	1.0 g
Copper(II) sulphate crystals	blue crystals	white powder	0.7 g

a Which of these substances does not change on heating?

1
Q6a

....

b Explain why copper increases in mass when heated in air but copper(II) carbonate decreases in mass.

4
Q6b

....

....

....

Heating copper(II) sulphate crystals causes a temporary change.

c Describe what you would see if cold water was dropped onto the white powder formed when copper(II) sulphate crystals are heated.

2
Q6c

Max. 13
Qs 5–6
subtotal

17

7 Look at the diagram of the human thorax and answer the questions below.

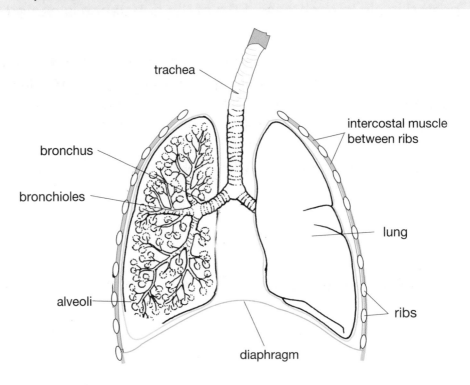

trachea

intercostal muscle between ribs

bronchus

bronchioles

lung

alveoli

ribs

diaphragm

1
Q7a(i)

a When a person breathes in, the diaphragm moves down.
(i) How does the ribcage move?

....

2
Q7a(ii)

(ii) Explain how air is forced into the lungs.

....

....

1
Q7b(i)

b Gas exchange takes place in the alveoli.
(i) Which gas from the air passes into the blood?

....

(ii) Which **two** waste products pass out of the blood and are breathed out?

2
Q7b(ii)

....

....

(iii) The alveoli have a very large surface area. Explain why a large surface area is needed.

1
Q7b(iii)

....

....

8 The pink colouring in rose petals can be used as an indicator for acids and alkalis. The colouring is not soluble in water but is soluble in ethanol.

a Describe how a solution of this pink colouring could be made from rose petals.

4
Q8a

....

....

....

Max. 11
Qs 7–8a
subtotal

b The table gives the colours of pink rose petal colouring, phenolphthalein and methyl orange indicators in acidic, neutral and alkaline solutions.

Indicator	Colour in acidic solution	Colour in neutral solution	Colour in alkaline solution
pink rose petal solution	pink	pink	green
phenolphthalein	colourless	colourless	pink
methyl orange	red	orange	orange

(i) What is the pH value of a neutral solution?

1
Q8b(i)

....

(ii) What colour would pink rose petal solution turn in sodium hydroxide solution?

1
Q8b(ii)

....

(iii) How can phenolphthalein and methyl orange indicators be used to show that a solution is neutral?

2
Q8b(iii)

....

....

4
Q9a

9 The diagrams on the next page show a plant cell and an animal cell.

a Use words from the list to label the diagrams. You may use each word once, more than once, or not at all.

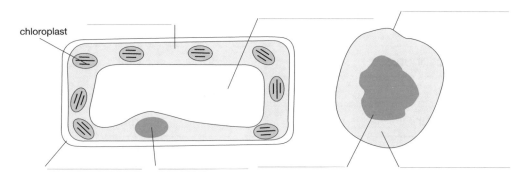

cell membrane   cell wall   cytoplasm
             nucleus   vacuole

chloroplast

b What is the job of the cell wall?

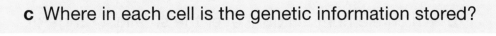

c Where in each cell is the genetic information stored?

Respiration takes place in all cells.
Use words from this list to answer the questions:

carbon dioxide   energy   glucose   oxygen   water

d Which two substances are used up during respiration?

.... and ....

e Which two substances are produced during respiration?

.... and ....

f What is released during respiration?

....

10 The table gives some information about five elements.

Element	Melting point in °C	Boiling point in °C	Dull or shiny	Electrical conductivity
Phosphorus	44	280	dull	nil
Iron	1535	3000	shiny	good
Mercury	−39	357	shiny	good
Sulphur	113	444	dull	nil
Sodium	98	890	shiny	good

a Which element is liquid at room temperature (20°C)?

....

b Which element is liquid over the smallest range of temperatures?

....

c The bar chart shows the boiling points of some of the elements.

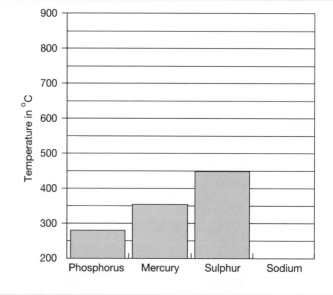

Draw the bar to show the boiling point of sodium.

d Which of these elements are metals and which are non-metals?

Metals...

Non-metals ....

2
Q10d

e Explain how you could separate iron from other elements.

....

....

2
Q10e

f Sodium and sulphur burn in oxygen to form oxides. How do these two oxides differ when universal indicator solution is added?

....

....

....

2
Q10f

Max. 9
Q 10
subtotal

2
Q11a

11 The diagram shows a drawing pin.

a What **two** features of the drawing pin enable it to exert a large pressure?

....

....

2
Q11b

b A tank weighs 60 000 N and the area of its caterpillar tracks touching the ground is 20 m^2.

Work out the pressure on the ground in N/m^2.

pressure = ... N/m^2.

12 The photo below shows an audience watching a play in a theatre.

a Underline in the list below the objects shown in the photo that give out light.

1
Q12a

actors   audience   stage lights

b Explain how a person in the audience sees the actors.

2
Q12b

....

....

c Stage lights are often fitted with colour filters. Underline in the list below the colours that can pass through a cyan (turquoise) filter.

2
Q12c

blue   cyan   green   magenta   red   yellow

1
Q12d

d An actress wears a yellow costume. The stage is lit with red light.
What colour does her costume appear to be?

Max. 10
Qs
11–12
subtotal

....

13 Five groups of students carried out an experiment. They burnt different masses of magnesium ribbon in air. Each group found the mass of magnesium oxide produced. The apparatus they used is shown in the diagram below.

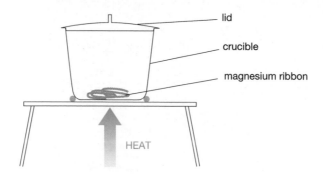

lid

crucible

magnesium ribbon

HEAT

2
Q13a

a Why is it necessary to lift the lid from time to time during the experiment but not to let any smoke out?

....

....

1
Q13b

The results of their experiments are shown in the graph on page 27.

b What mass of magnesium did Group B use?

....

1
Q13c

c What mass of oxygen combined with the magnesium in Group B's experiment?

....

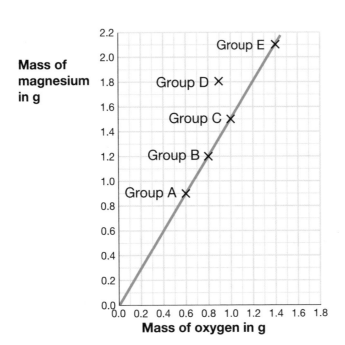

Mass of magnesium in g (y-axis from 0.0 to 2.2)

Group E ✗
Group D ✗
Group C ✗
Group B ✗
Group A ✗

Mass of oxygen in g (x-axis from 0.0 to 1.8)

d (i) Why do you think there was unreacted magnesium left in the crucible after Group D's experiment?

◆
1
Q13d(i)

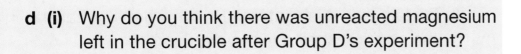

(ii) Describe a test you would use to show that there was unreacted magnesium left.

2
Q13d(ii)

Test ....

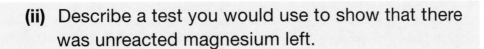

Result ....

1
Q13e

e Write down the chemical formula for magnesium oxide.

Max. 8
Q 13
subtotal

....

27

14 The diagram shows the Earth at one position in its orbit.

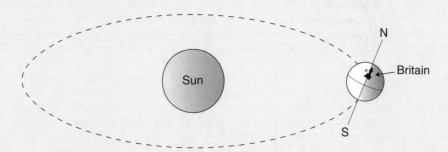

a What causes the Earth to have different seasons at different positions in its orbit?

....

b Explain why it is winter in Britain when the Earth is in the position shown in the diagram.

....

....

15 Below is a list of energy sources.
  a Underline the non-renewable energy sources.

biomass   **coal**   **oil**   **wind**

b A new power station is built that will grow its own fuel: wood from fast-growing willow trees.
  (i) Explain whether wood is a renewable or non-renewable energy source.

....

....

(ii) Give **one** advantage of using wood as a fuel to generate electricity.

1
Q15b(ii)

....

16 John and Rebecca are planning an experiment using leaves. They want to find out when leaves produce carbon dioxide and when they use it up.

They use an indicator to help them. The colour of the indicator is:

- blue when there is very little carbon dioxide present
- green when there is a small amount of carbon dioxide present
- yellow when there is a lot of carbon dioxide present.

The diagram shows the experiment that they plan to set up. They plan to shine a bright light on the tubes for several hours and look for changes in the colour of the indicator.

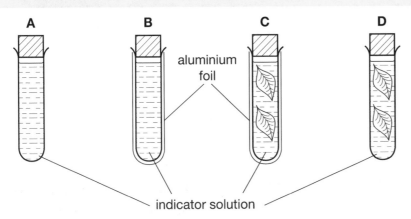

a In their plan, John and Rebecca intend to keep some things the same for all the tubes. State **three** things that they should keep the same for each tube.

◆ 3
Q16a

1 ....

2 ....

3 ....

Max. 10
Qs
14–16a
subtotal

29

1
Q16b

b Why did John and Rebecca not put any leaves in tubes A and B?

....

Tube	Colour of indicator	
	At the start	**After a few hours**
A	green	green
B	green	green
C	green	yellow
D	green	blue

4
Q16c

c The table shows the results.
Explain why the indicator changed colour in tubes C and D.

Tube C ....

....

Tube D ....

17 A lump of calcium carbonate is added to dilute hydrochloric acid. Bubbles of carbon dioxide gas are seen. Calcium chloride and water are also formed.

a Write a word equation for the reaction.

2
Q17a

....

b Write down the chemical formula of carbon dioxide.

1
Q17b

....

c How would you test for carbon dioxide?

Test ....

Result ....

d Describe how you could use an experiment like this to compare the rates of reaction of calcium carbonate as a lump and as a powder.

....

....

....

18 An iron bar is placed inside a coil of wire connected, through a switch, to a battery. A magnetic compass is placed at each end of the bar.

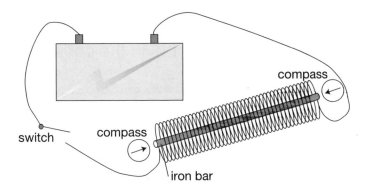

switch   compass   compass

iron bar

When the switch is open, both compasses point towards the iron bar.

a What difference, if any, would be noticed if a brass bar were used instead of an iron bar?

....

1
Q18b

b Describe what happens to the compasses when the switch is closed.

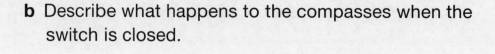

....

1
Q18c

c Explain why this happens.

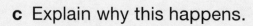

....

19 The diagram shows a lamp connected in a circuit.

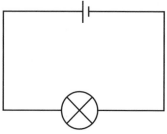

2
Q19a

a An ammeter is used to measure the current in a circuit. Draw the symbol in the correct position on the diagram.

2
Q19b

b What could you use to measure the voltage across the lamp? Draw the symbol in the correct position on the diagram.

1
Q19c

....

c Explain how increasing the number of cells connected in series affects the current in the lamp.

....

START
FINISH

1 The diagram shows the magnetic field pattern of a bar magnet.

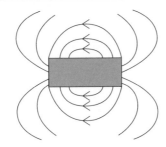

   a Label the poles on the magnet.

   b The diagram shows two magnets that are repelling each other.

      (i) Label the poles on the right-hand magnet.

      (ii) Draw an arrow on the diagram that shows the force on the right-hand magnet.

2 The diagrams at the top of page 34 show three methods that can be used to separate mixtures of substances.

   a Match up the name of the method with the correct diagram by writing the letters **Q**, **R** and **S** in the boxes.

Name of the method	Letter
Chromatography	
Distillation	
Fractional distillation	

1
Q1a

1
Q1b(i)

1
Q1b(ii)

3
Q2a

Max. 6
Qs 1–2a
subtotal

33

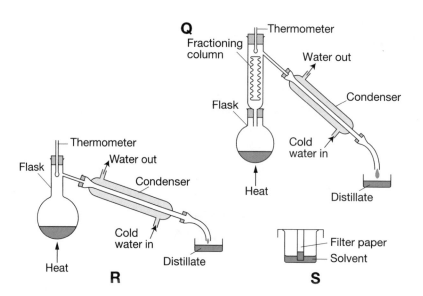

b Here is a list of mixtures that could be separated.

A A solution of wax dissolved in hexane.

B A mixture of a solid residue and water.

C A mixture of coloured dyes in solution.

D A mixture of two liquids, hexane and heptane.

1
Q2b(i)

(i) Which mixture could be separated by chromatography?

1
Q2b(ii)

(ii) Which mixture could be separated by fractional distillation?

c Some copper(II) sulphate is dissolved in cold water until no more will dissolve.
(i) What name is given to a solution when no more solute will dissolve?

1
Q2c(i)

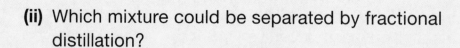

(ii) How can more copper(II) sulphate be made to dissolve in the same amount of water?

....

3 This diagram shows part of a food web.

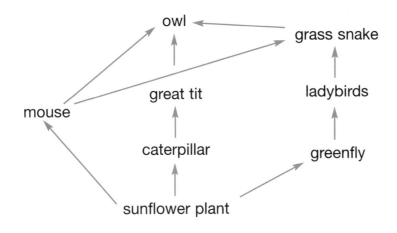

a Name one herbivore shown in the food web.

....

b During one summer there is a shortage of ladybirds. Explain why this has little effect on the number of grass snakes.

....

c Explain why the great tit is both a predator and prey.

....

Max. 8
Qs 2b–3
subtotal

35

....

4   This question is about how smoking cigarettes during pregnancy can affect the birthweight of babies.

The table shows the average number of cigarettes smoked each day by pregnant women and the average birthweights of their babies.

Average number of cigarettes smoked each day by pregnant women	Average birthweight of their babies in g
0	3000
10	2990
20	2965
30	2910
40	2800

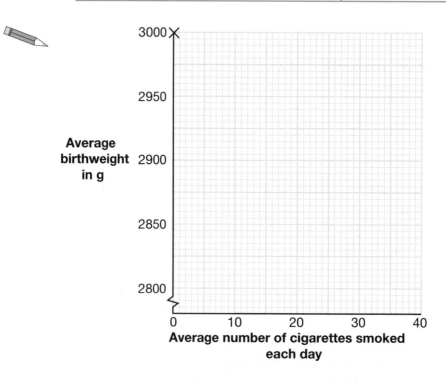

a Plot the values in the table on the grid. The first one has been done for you.

b Finish the graph by drawing the best line.

c From your graph find the number of cigarettes that produces an average birthweight of 2900 g.

....

d Smoking during pregnancy can harm the unborn baby. Write down one other habit a pregnant woman might have that could harm her unborn baby.

....

5 The diagram shows three circuits.

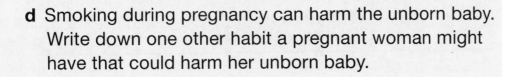

Circuit A   Circuit B   Circuit C

a What could you use to measure the current in circuit A? Draw the symbol on the diagram.

....

b In which circuit do the cells run down the quickest?

....

c Explain why this happens in this circuit.

Max. 10
Q4–5
subtotal

37

....

6 Experiments were carried out with four metals – **W**, **X**, **Y** and **Z**. The diagrams show the results obtained when a piece of each metal was added to dilute hydrochloric acid. Three of the test tubes were then heated and the results are shown below. Answer the questions below.

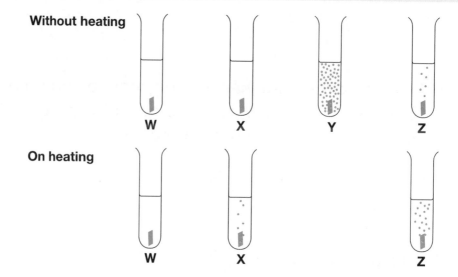

a Use the results of these reactions to put these four metals in order of decreasing reactivity.

Most reactive   Least reactive

3 Q6a

b (i) Write down the name of the gas formed when Y reacts with dilute hydrochloric acid.

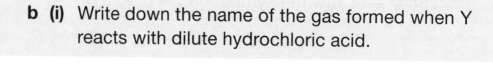

1 Q6b(i)

(ii) How would you test for this gas?

2 Q6b(ii)

Test ....

Result ....

7 The diagram shows some of the organs in a human body. Draw lines between the tables to match the letter of of each organ to the job it does.

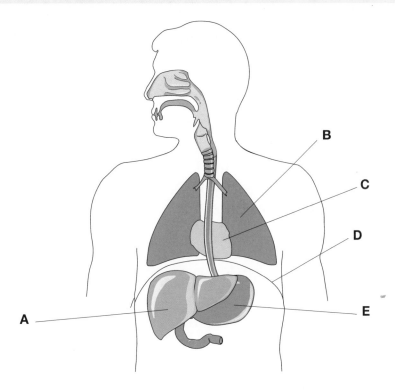

Organ	Job of the organ
A	pumps blood around the body
B	processes nitrogen waste (urea)
C	helps to inflate and deflate the lungs
D	digests food
E	exchanges gases between air and blood

5
Q7

Max. 11
Qs 6–7
subtotal

8 Iron and sulphur are elements. When they are mixed together and the mixture is heated in a test tube, a reaction takes place. A glow spreads throughout the mixture even if the test tube is taken out of the flame.

a What does the glow spreading through the mixture show about the reaction?

....

b Write down the name of the compound formed when iron and sulphur combine.

....

c In the diagram below:

● stands for a zinc atom   ○ stands for a sulphur atom

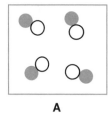 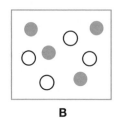  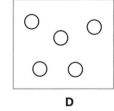

    A   B   C   D

(i) Which diagram represents pure sulphur?

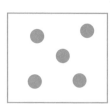

(ii) Which diagram represents a mixture of zinc and sulphur?

1 Q8a

1 Q8b

1 Q8c(i)

1 Q8c(ii)

(iii) Which diagram represents a compound of zinc and sulphur?

1
Q8c(iii)

9 The diagram shows a boat floating on water. The arrow represents one of the forces that acts on the boat.

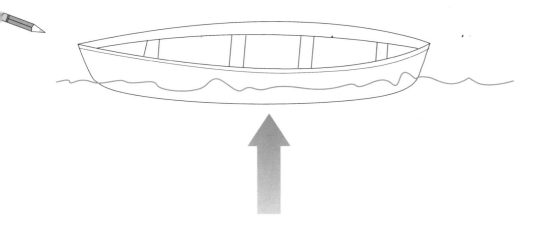

a Choose words from the list below to complete the sentence that describes the force.

boat   **downward**   **Earth**   **upward**   **water**

The arrow shows the .... push of the

.... on the ....

3
Q9a

b Draw an arrow on the diagram to show another force that acts on the boat when it is floating.

1
Q9b

Max. 9
Qs 8–9b
subtotal

41

1
Q9c

c Two people climb into the boat. How does this affect the size of the downward force?

....

1
Q9d

d How does this affect the size of the upward force?

....

10 The diagram shows part of an arm.

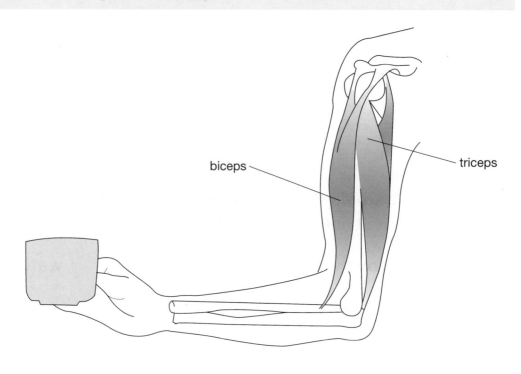

biceps

triceps

1
Q10a

a What type of joint is the shoulder?

....

1
Q10b

b Why is this type of joint found at the shoulder?

....

c Use the words *contract* and *relax* to describe what happens to the biceps and triceps when the cup is lifted.

2
Q10c

....

....

11 A balanced diet contains the following food chemicals.

**carbohydrate   fat   fibre   minerals
protein   vitamins   water**

a Which of these is the main food chemical provided by bread and pasta?

1
Q11a

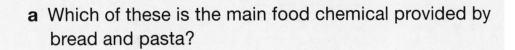
....

b Which of these provides a long-term energy store?

1
Q11b

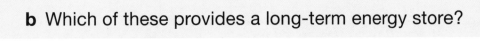
....

Max. 8
Qs
9c–11b
subtotal

2
Q11c

c The names of three important food chemicals are shown in the boxes below left. Three foods are shown on the right.
Draw lines to link each food chemical to the best supply of that chemical.

fat

 fish

protein

 fruit

vitamins

 cheese

1
Q11d

d Explain why fibre is an important part of a balanced diet.

....

....

12 Ice, liquid water and steam all contain the same water particles.

a Describe the arrangement and movement of particles in liquid water.

4
Q12a

Arrangement ....

....

Movement ....

....

MARKS

b When a saucer filled with liquid water is left on a window sill, the water evaporates.

(i) Explain in terms of particles and energy what is happening when liquid water evaporates.

2
Q12b(i)

....

....

(ii) Why does evaporation occur faster when there is a draught in the room?

1
Q12b(ii)

....

....

(iii) In certain hot countries, a thin layer of oil is put onto the surface of the water in reservoirs. How does this affect evaporation of the water?

1
Q12b(iii)

....

....

13 a The diagram shows xylem from the stem of a plant.

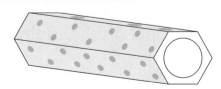

1
Q13a(i)

(i) What substance is transported by the xylem?

Max. 12
Qs
11c–13a(i)
subtotal

45

....

1
Q13a(ii)

(ii) Which part of the plant does this substance come from?

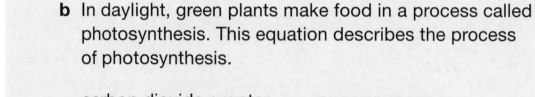

....

b In daylight, green plants make food in a process called photosynthesis. This equation describes the process of photosynthesis.

carbon dioxide + water $\longrightarrow$ sugar + oxygen

(i) What waste product is produced during photosynthesis?

1
Q13b(i)

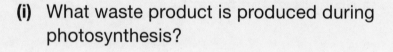

....

2
Q13b(ii)

(ii) How does the plant get rid of this waste product?

....

....

1
Q13b(iii)

(iii) What is the energy source for photosynthesis?

....

1
Q13c

c Some ivy plants have leaves that are green and yellow. Which part of the leaf produces the most sugar?

....

d The graph shows how the amount of sugar produced by a tomato plant growing in a greenhouse changes over a period of several days.

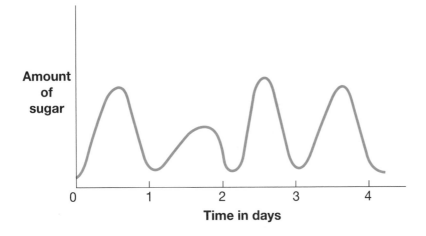

(i) Explain why the rate of sugar production varies.

1
Q13d(i)

....

(ii) How could the tomato grower change the air in the greenhouse to increase the rate of sugar production?

1
Q13d(ii)

....

Max. 8
Qs
13a(ii)–
13d(ii)
subtotal

14 The diagram shows the driving force and the resistive force acting on a yacht.

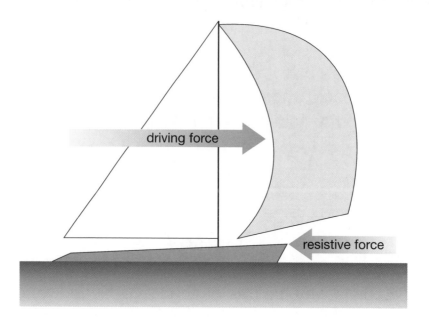

driving force

resistive force

a What causes the driving force?

....

b Explain why the yacht is speeding up.

....

c Explain what happens to the speed of the yacht when the sail is lowered.

....

....

....

15 Asif and Bella have three brands of indigestion tablets.
They are called Easytum, Calmers and Soothies.
The tablets of each brand have the same mass.
They want to know which brand contains the most antacid.
They plan to drop tablets of each brand into dilute hydrochloric acid and see how many tablets react.
In each case the acid is at room temperature.

a Suggest **two** things they should do to make sure this is a fair test.

2
Q15a

(i) ....

(ii) ....

b How could they use the results to work out which tablet contains the most antacid?

2
Q15b

c Bella suggests that the experiment would be better if the tablets were crushed up.
Suggest one advantage this might have and one disadvantage.

2
Q15c

Advantage ....

Max. 10
Qs
14a–15
subtotal

Disadvantage ....

1
Q16a

16 a The diagram below shows four different reflections of light at a mirror. Which one is correct?

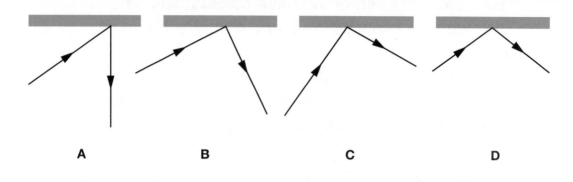

A   B   C   D

1
Q16b

b Explain how the reflection of light by a page of this book is different from the reflection of light at a mirror.

....

1
Q16c

c A candle is placed in front of a mirror. Which letter shows the position of the image of the candle?

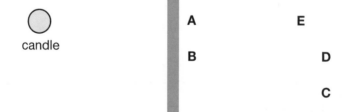

candle

A   E

B   D

C

d Write down **two** ways in which the candle and its image are similar.

2
Q16d

....

....

17 a The photo shows a loudspeaker. How does the loudspeaker produce a sound wave?

1
Q17a

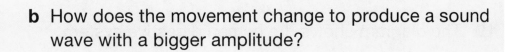

....

....

b How does the movement change to produce a sound wave with a bigger amplitude?

1
Q17b

....

....

c How does the sound change when the amplitude of the sound wave is increased?

1
Q17c

....

Max. 8
Qs
16a–17
subtotal

1
Q18a

18 a The diagram shows a satellite in orbit around the Earth. Use an arrow to show the force that acts on the satellite.

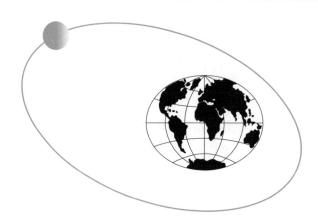

2
Q18b

b Write down **two** uses of artificial satellites.

....

....

....

19 The diagram shows the human digestive system.

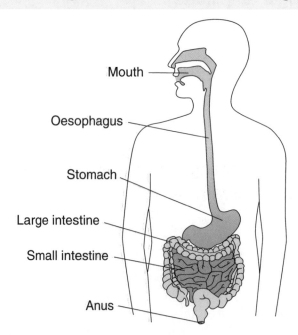

Mouth

Oesophagus

Stomach

Large intestine

Small intestine

Anus

a Match each named organ with its job. Draw a line from each organ to the job it does. One has been done for you.

5
Q19a

Organ	Job of the organ
Anus	absorbs dissolved food into the blood
Oesophagus	chews the food into small pieces
Large intestine	digests protein
Mouth	passes the food to the stomach
Small intestine	excretes waste
Stomach	absorbs water from the waste

b The process of digestion starts in the mouth. What is present in saliva to start the process of digestion?

1
Q19b

....

c Sugar molecules are absorbed into the bloodstream but starch molecules are not. Explain why.

2
Q19c

....

....

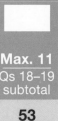

Max. 11
Qs 18–19
subtotal

53

20 **a** The diagram below shows a rock exposed to air and water. At night the temperature drops below 0°C. During the day the temperature rises to 20°C.

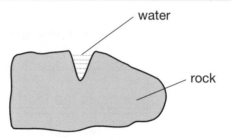

3
Q20a(i)

(i) Explain how this rock is broken up.

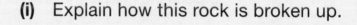

....

....

....

1
Q20a(ii)

(ii) What name is given to this process?

....

4
Q20b

b Rocks are broken down in a desert without the help of water. Explain **two** ways rocks can be broken down without water in the desert.

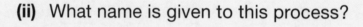

....

....

....

21 Below is a diagram showing two blocks of glass.

a Complete the diagram to show how white light passes through the rectangular blocks.

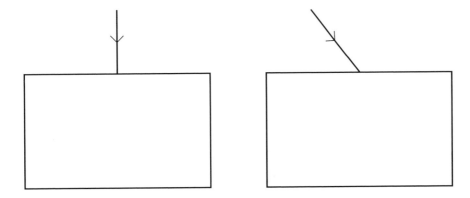

b As the light enters and leaves the glass its speed changes. What name is given to this effect?

....

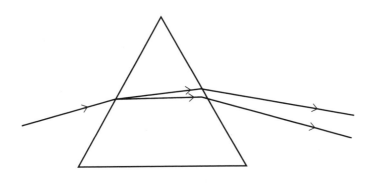

c White light can be dispersed as it passes through a triangular prism.

(i) What happens to white light when it is dispersed?

....

(ii) What does dispersion show about the nature of white light?

....

2
Q22a

22 On a clear night, stars, planets and the Moon can be
seen in the sky. Stars are seen by the light they give out.
a Describe how the Moon is seen.

....

....

....

b An astronomer takes a photograph of the sky at night.
Three hours later, she takes another photograph of
the same part of the sky. These are the photographs.

(i) Which star appears in the same position?

1
Q22b(i)

....

1
Q22b(ii)

(ii) Explain why the other stars appear to have moved.

....

1
Q22b(iii)

(iii) After taking the second photograph, how long
would the astronomer have to wait to be able to
see the stars in the same position as they were in
the first photograph?

Max. 5
Q 22
subtotal

....

Answers

HOW TO MARK THE TESTS

When marking the tests remember that the answers given are sample answers. You must look at your answers and judge whether they deserve credit. If they do, then award the mark.

You should pay special attention to spelling. There is no automatic penalty for a word that is misspelt. Look at the word as written and read it aloud. If it sounds correct and has the correct number of syllables, the mark can be awarded. For example, 'desolve' and 'weit' are acceptable for 'dissolve' and 'weight'. However, 'photosis' would not be accepted for 'photosynthesis'.

There is an emphasis on the correct spelling of scientific words. Look through this book and make a list of scientific words. Reviewing this list in the days before the tests is good preparation.

When you go through the answers, try to work out where you have gone wrong. Make a note of the key points, so that you will remember them next time.

Enter your marks for each test on the Marking grid on page 75, and then work out your level of achievement in these tests on page 74.

QUICK QUESTIONS   PAGES 8–10

Life processes and living things
1 kidney
2 water and carbon dioxide
3 protein
4 nucleus
5 plant
6 hinge
7 glucose and oxygen
8 inheritance
9 they have a large surface area
10 in the testes

Materials and their properties
1 gas
2 atom
3 carbon dioxide
4 chromatography
5 hydrogen
6 iron
7 7
8 saturated
9 physical
10 acid

Physical processes
1 series
2 parallel
3 amp
4 it transfers energy from the source to the components
5 moment/torque/leverage
6 pressure
7 a star
8 one day/24 hours
9 unbalanced
10 by increasing the frequency/more vibrations per second

57

Test A: Pages 12–32

1 a By radiation   *1 mark*

Energy can be transferred from hot objects by conduction, convection and radiation. Of these methods, only radiation does not rely on the movement of particles, so it is the only method of energy transfer that takes place through a vacuum.

b kinetic   *1 mark*
  electricity   *1 mark*
c From gravitational potential energy   *1 mark*
  to kinetic energy   *1 mark*

TOTAL 5 MARKS

Gravitational potential energy is often abbreviated to potential energy or gpe.

2 a The leaves are close to the ground.   *1 mark*
  The flowers have short stalks.   *1 mark*

Both of these adaptations enable the daisy to survive the effects of a lawnmower.

b They have a large surface area.   *1 mark*
c Water and minerals (or a named mineral such as nitrogen, phosphorus
  or potassium)   *1 mark each: 2 marks*
d Photosynthesis takes place in the chloroplasts.   *1 mark*
  This takes place in the leaves.   *1 mark*

TOTAL 7 MARKS

3 a A – placenta; B – amniotic sac; C – amniotic fluid   *3 marks*
b The umbilical cord takes oxygen and nutrients to the fetus   *1 mark*
  and also passes waste products from the fetus to the mother.   *1 mark*

Students frequently score the first mark but do not score the second. The indication of two marks for the question should help suggest the second statement.

c A male sex cell (sperm) and a female sex cell (egg) join together.   *1 mark*
d In the egg tube (Fallopian tube)   *1 mark*

TOTAL 7 MARKS

Test A: Answers

4 a   Natalie   *1 mark*

Natalie was the fastest because she completed the race in the shortest time.

b   Claire   *1 mark*

Claire took the longest time to complete the same distance as the other swimmers.

c   speed = distance ÷ time   *1 mark*
speed = 80 m ÷ 20 s = 4 (m/s)   *1 mark*

When doing calculations you should always write out the formula first. This way, a mark is gained for knowing the formula even if a mistake is made when working out the answer.

TOTAL 4 MARKS

5 a (i)   **A**   *1 mark*

A series circuit is one where there is only one current path. A parallel circuit has two or more current paths.

(ii)   **A**   *1 mark*
(iii)   **A and C**   *1 mark*
b   Ammeter   *1 mark*
c   None   *1 mark*

Lamps, motors and other circuit components do not use up current. The current that passes into any component in a circuit is equal to the current that passes out.

d   Increase the voltage/decrease the resistance of the lamp   *1 mark*

The answer 'use a bigger battery' does not gain a mark, since it is the voltage that counts, not the physical size of the battery. Removing the motor is also wrong, as it is not in the same current path as the lamp.

TOTAL 6 MARKS

6	**a**	Copper(II) oxide	*1 mark*
	b	Copper reacts with oxygen in the air.	*1 mark*
		Black coating is copper(II) oxide	*1 mark*
		Copper(II) carbonate decomposes (splits up)	*1 mark*
		Produces carbon dioxide which is lost	*1 mark*
	c	Any two from:	
		turns blue, steam produced, heat given off	*2 marks*

This question is about permanent and temporary changes that take place when substances are heated. A temporary change is one which can be reversed easily. For example, if ice is heated it turns to liquid water; if water is cooled, ice is reformed.

A permanent change is one which cannot be reversed, either by cooling or by mixing the products. For example, burning a piece of wood is a permanent change.

TOTAL 7 MARKS

7 a (i) The ribcage moves upwards and outwards. *1 mark*

This movement is caused by the contraction of the intercostal muscles. It is important to remember that muscles can only pull, they cannot push. During inhalation (breathing in) the muscles contract to lift the ribcage.

(ii)	The pressure of the air in the lungs is reduced.	*1 mark*
	The greater pressure of the air outside the lungs pushes air in.	*1 mark*
b (i)	Oxygen	*1 mark*

Oxygen is needed for all cells to respire.

(ii) Carbon dioxide (1) and water (1) *2 marks*

Carbon dioxide and water are the waste products of respiration.

(iii) So that a large volume of gases can be exchanged in a short time. *1 mark*

The alveoli are adapted to the job that they do by having a very large surface area for gas exchange to take place.

TOTAL 7 MARKS

Test A: Answers

8	**a**	Cut up or crush up rose petals.	*1 mark*
		Add ethanol to petals.	*1 mark*
		Heat (using a water bath).	*1 mark*
		Filter off (or decant off) remains of petals.	*1 mark*
	b (i)	pH 7	*1 mark*
	(ii)	Green	*1 mark*
	(iii)	In separate tests, phenolphthalein is colourless	*1 mark*
		and methyl orange is orange.	*1 mark*

Examiner's tip

In part **a** the answer could include some indication of hazards of heating ethanol with a naked flame.

In **b(iii)** the marks can only be awarded if it is appreciated that both colours are obtained. It is this combination that tells us the solution is neutral. Colourless and red solutions would indicate an acid and pink and orange solutions would indicate an alkali.

TOTAL 8 MARKS

9 a   Seven correct labels.   *4 marks*

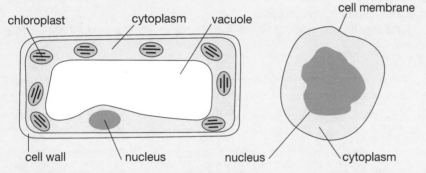

Count up number of correct labels, divide by two and round up to whole number.

	b	To maintain the cell's shape and rigidity	*1 mark*
	c	In the nucleus.	*1 mark*
	d	glucose; oxygen	*2 marks*
	e	carbon dioxide; water	*2 marks*
	f	energy	*1 mark*

Examiner's tip

It is important to be able to distinguish plant and animal cells. Plant cells have a cell wall, which gives the cell shape and some rigidity.

TOTAL 11 MARKS

10 a Mercury 　　　　　　　　　　　　　　　　　　　　*1 mark*
b Phosphorus 　　　　　　　　　　　　　　　　　　　　*1 mark*
c

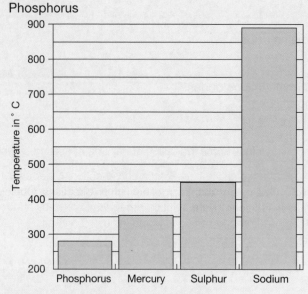

1 mark

d Metals – iron, mercury and sodium
Non-metals – phosphorus, sulphur 　　　　　　　　　*2 marks*
One mark for a correct list of metals and one for a correct list of non-metals.

You do not need to remember whether the elements are metals or non-metals. The properties in the table will help you decide. One problem caused by the marking scheme is that one error, e.g. writing that mercury is a non-metal, will cost both marks.

e Use a magnet. 　　　　　　　　　　　　　　　　　　*1 mark*
Iron will be attracted to the magnet but the others will not. 　*1 mark*

Many students lose the second mark here. They refer to the magnet but do not explain how it is used to separate the iron.

f Sodium oxide turns universal indicator purple (strongly alkaline). 　*1 mark*
Sulphur dioxide turns universal indicator red (strongly acidic). 　*1 mark*

Non-metals burn to form acidic oxides. Metals burn to form neutral or alkaline oxides. A reactive metal, such as sodium, forms an alkaline oxide.

TOTAL 9 MARKS

11 a The flat head (allows larger force by thumb) 　　　　　*1 mark*
and the sharp point. 　　　　　　　　　　　　　　　*1 mark*
b pressure = force ÷ area 　　　　　　　　　　　　　　*1 mark*
pressure = 60 000 N ÷ 20 m² = 3000 (N/m²) 　　　　*1 mark*

Test A: Answers

This is another example where the formula used should be written down before doing the calculation.

TOTAL 4 MARKS

12 a stage lights   *1 mark*
b Light from the stage lights is reflected by the actor.   *1 mark*
This reflected light enters the eyes of the audience.   *1 mark*

Mirrors and other shiny surfaces only reflect light in one direction. Other everyday objects scatter the light. This means that they reflect it in all directions. Objects that are not light sources are seen by the light that they scatter.

c blue, cyan and green   *2 marks*

Award one mark for getting two colours correct.

d red   *1 mark*

The yellow costume reflects red, green and yellow light. As yellow and green are not present in red light, it can only reflect the red.

TOTAL 6 MARKS

13 a The lid has to be lifted to allow air (oxygen) to enter the crucible.   *1 mark*
If smoke is lost the mass of the magnesium oxide is reduced.   *1 mark*
b 1.2 g   *1 mark*
c 0.8 g   *1 mark*

The answers to parts **b** and **c** can be obtained from the graph. Always give the units.

d (i) Their point is not on the line and there is less oxygen than would be expected. *1 mark*
(ii) Add hydrochloric acid to the residue.   *1 mark*
Bubbles of colourless gas are formed.   *1 mark*

Hydrochloric acid reacts with excess magnesium to form hydrogen gas. No gas is formed when magnesium oxide reacts with hydrochloric acid.

e MgO *1 mark*

The formula shows that one atom of oxygen reacts with each atom of magnesium.

TOTAL 8 MARKS

14 a   The Earth's tilt on its axis.   *1 mark*

The varying distance of the Earth from the Sun has only a minor effect. The main cause of seasons is the Earth's tilt.

b   The northern hemisphere is tilted away from the Sun,   *1 mark*
so energy from the Sun is spread over a larger area than in the   *1 mark*
Southern hemisphere

If you answered in **b** that there are fewer hours of daylight, this is correct and should be awarded the second mark.

TOTAL 3 MARKS

15 a   coal and oil   *One mark each: 2 marks*
b (i)   Wood is renewable because more can be grown.   *1 mark*

Do not award a mark for the answer that wood is renewable. The reason why wood is renewable is also needed, since the question asks you to 'explain'.

(ii)   Fewer fossil fuels such as coal need to be burned.   *1 mark*

Award a mark for an answer along the lines that coal or other fossil fuels will last longer.

TOTAL 4 MARKS

16 a   Any three from: distance from the lamp, volume of indicator solution used, area of the leaves, the time the tubes are exposed to the light. 1 mark each.   *3 marks*

When planning a fair test, you need to identify all the factors that need to be controlled.

b   A and B act as controls.   *1 mark*

A and B were used to show there would be no changes in indicator without leaves being present.

c   Tube C – the change from green to yellow shows that the level of carbon dioxide has increased.   *1 mark*
This is because respiration produces carbon dioxide.   *1 mark*
Tube D – the change from green to blue shows that the level of carbon dioxide has decreased.   *1 mark*
Photosynthesis has used up the carbon dioxide.   *1 mark*

Pupils often forget that respiration takes place in plants both in and out of the light. However, in bright light the effect of respiration is swamped by that of the photosynthesis taking place.

TOTAL 8 MARKS

17 a   calcium carbonate + hydrochloric acid → carbon dioxide + calcium chloride
+ water (1 mark for each side of the equation correct)   *2 marks*

b CO_2 *1 mark*

You need to be able to write down the chemical formula of simple compounds. Pupils often write down the formula of carbon dioxide as CO2 and C_2O. Neither of these would gain a mark.

c   Bubble the gas through lime water.   *1 mark*
      The lime water turns milky.   *1 mark*
d   Use the same mass of calcium carbonate lump and powder.   *1 mark*
      Add to the same volume of acid of the same concentration.   *1 mark*
      The one that reacts faster is the one that produces more bubbles in a given
      time OR finishes reacting in the shorter time.   *1 mark*

It is important that you state here how you would tell which one reacts faster.

TOTAL 8 MARKS

18 a   The compasses would not point towards the bar. They would point North.   *1 mark*

Iron is a magnetic material; brass is not. The compasses are attracted to the iron, but not the brass bar.

b   One points towards the bar and one points away from it.   *1 mark*
c   The bar has become a temporary magnet.   *1 mark*

When the iron is a magnet it has two opposite poles. One repels the N-seeking pole of a compass and the other attracts the N-seeking pole of a compass.

TOTAL 3 MARKS

19 a   An A drawn in a circle.   *1 mark*
      In series, either side of the lamp.   *1 mark*

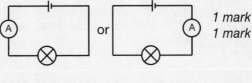

b   A voltmeter   *1 mark*
      The symbol should be drawn as a V in
      a circle, in parallel with the lamp.   *1 mark*

Ammeters are always connected in series with the current being measured. Voltmeters are connected in parallel with a battery (to measure its voltage) or a circuit component (to measure the voltage across it).

c The voltage is increased; this causes the current to increase. *1 mark*

In a series circuit, the battery voltage is shared between the components. The greater the voltage, the greater the current.

TOTAL 5 MARKS
TEST TOTAL 120 MARKS

Test B: Pages 33–56

1 a The left-hand side of the magnet should be labelled S, and the right-hand side N. *1 mark*

The direction of a magnetic field is the direction of the force on the N-seeking pole of another magnet, so it points away from the N-seeking pole and towards the S-seeking pole.

b (i) The left-hand side of the magnet should be labelled N, and the right-hand side S. *1 mark*
(ii) The arrow should point from left to right. *1 mark*

TOTAL 3 MARKS

2 a S, R, Q *3 marks*
(All correct – 3 marks, two correct – 2 marks, one correct – 1 mark)
b (i) C *1 mark*
(ii) D *1 mark*

Fractional distillation is used to separate a mixture of liquids with different boiling points, e.g. hexane and heptane.

c (i) Saturated. *1 mark*
(ii) By heating the water. *1 mark*

Using powdered copper sulphate or stirring the mixture will speed up the dissolving but not make any more dissolve.

TOTAL 7 MARKS

3 a Mouse **or** caterpillar **or** greenfly *1 mark*

A herbivore is an animal that only eats plants.

b   The grass snakes have other food that they eat.   *1 mark*

c   The great tit is a predator as it feeds on caterpillars.   *1 mark*

    The great tit is the prey of the owl.   *1 mark*

TOTAL 4 MARKS

4 a   Four points correctly plotted.   *2 marks*

Allow one mark for two or three correctly plotted points.

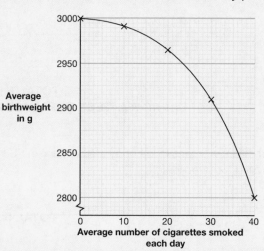

b   Correctly drawn curve.   *1 mark*

c   31 cigarettes   *1 mark*

Examiner's tip

The best line is a curve and not a straight line. The examiner reads the answer from the graph which you have drawn.

d   Drinking alcohol or taking drugs.   *1 mark*

TOTAL 5 MARKS

5 a   An ammeter   *1 mark*

    The symbol should be drawn as an A in a circle, between the lamp and either side of the cell.   *1 mark*

b   Circuit B   *1 mark*

c   This circuit has the greatest current.   *1 mark*

    There is a higher voltage for each lamp than in the other circuits.   *1 mark*

Examiner's tip

In a series circuit, the battery voltage is shared between the components. The greater the voltage, the greater the current

TOTAL 5 MARKS

6 a   **Y Z X W**   *3 marks*

*Award 1 mark if **Y** is before **Z**, 1 mark if **Z** is before **X** and 1 mark if **X** is before **W**.*

*So **Y, W, X, Z** is worth 1 mark for **Y** before **Z**.*

b (i)   Hydrogen   *1 mark*

    (ii)   Put a lighted splint into the gas.   *1 mark*

    Gas burns with a squeaky pop.   *1 mark*

Test B: Answers

Examiner's tip

Common errors are writing glowing splint (used for oxygen), or a splint (not suggesting it is lit) instead of lighted splint, or forgetting to write the result.

TOTAL 6 MARKS

7 The correct links are:
  A – processes nitrogen waste (urea)
  B – exchanges gases between air and blood
  C – pumps blood around the body
  D – expands and contracts the lungs
  E – digests food   *One mark for each one correct: 5 marks*

Examiner's tip

Questions about the jobs of different organs in the body are common in KS3 tests. Make sure that they are revised thoroughly.

TOTAL 5 MARKS

8 a	It is an exothermic reaction. It gives off energy.	*1 mark*
b	Iron sulphide or iron(II) sulphide	*1 mark*
c (i)	D	*1 mark*
(ii)	B	*1 mark*
(iii)	A	*1 mark*

Examiner's tip

Understanding how atoms of different elements combine together in fixed numbers to form a compound is an important idea that some students fail to understand at KS3.

TOTAL 5 MARKS

9 a	upward; water; boat	*One mark each: 3 marks*
b	The arrow should point vertically downwards from the centre of the boat.	*1 mark*

Examiner's tip

This force is the downward pull of the Earth. When the boat is floating, the vertical forces are balanced. This means that the downward pull of the Earth is equal in size to the upward push of the water.

c	It becomes bigger.	*1 mark*
d	It becomes bigger.	*1 mark*

Examiner's tip

When the downward force increases, the boat sinks further into the water. This causes the upward force to increase.

TOTAL 6 MARKS

10 a	Ball and socket	*1 mark*
b	It allows all-around movement of the arm.	*1 mark*

 Hinge joints such as the elbow and the knee allow movement in one dimension only.

c   The biceps contracts.   *1 mark*
        The triceps relaxes.   *1 mark*

Like a piece of string, muscles can only pull. They cannot push. A muscle contracts when it is pulling and is relaxed when it is not pulling. The biceps and triceps are known as an antagonistic pair of muscles because they pull in opposite directions.

TOTAL 4 MARKS

11 a   Carbohydrate   *1 mark*
b   Fat   *1 mark*
c   The correctly completed diagram is:

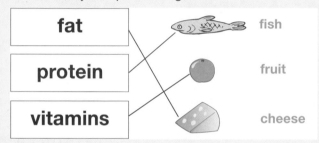

Allow 1 mark for 1 or 2 correct links.   *2 marks*
d   Fibre helps to keep food moving through the digestive system.   *1 mark*

Cheese provides both protein and fat. In this question you are asked to link each food chemical to the best supply. Of the foods given, cheese is the best supply of fat. This shows how important it is to read to the end of the question before attempting an answer.

TOTAL 5 MARKS

12 a   The arrangement of particles in liquid water is irregular;   *1 mark*
           the particles are close together.   *1 mark*
           The movement is random,   *1 mark*
           with frequent collisions.   *1 mark*

Be sure to distinguish arrangement and movement.

b (i)   Particles are escaping from the liquid into the air above.   *1 mark*
            It is the higher energy particles that are escaping.   *1 mark*

It is because it is the higher energy particles that escape that we notice a cooling effect on evaporation, e.g. when applying perfume.

(ii)   The particles escaping from the liquid are blown away and cannot   *1 mark*
           return to the liquid.
(iii) The layer of oil reduces evaporation by stopping the particles from
           escaping from the liquid.   *1 mark*

TOTAL 8 MARKS

13 a (i) Water   *1 mark*
   (ii) The root   *1 mark*

Examiner's tip

Water and other minerals from the soil are absorbed by the root hairs.

b (i) Oxygen   *1 mark*
   (ii) It diffuses into the air   *1 mark*
        through the stomata in the leaves.   *1 mark*

Examiner's tip

Gas exchange between a plant and the air takes place through the stomata. These are found mainly on the underneath of leaves. They are opened and closed by guard cells.

   (iii) Light **or** sunlight **or** the Sun   *1 mark*
   c The green part   *1 mark*

Examiner's tip

The green colour in plants is due to the substance chlorophyll. This absorbs the energy needed for photosynthesis.

d (i) The light level changes *or* the temperature changes.   *1 mark*
   (ii) The grower could increase the concentration of carbon dioxide.   *1 mark*

TOTAL 9 MARKS

14 a The wind   *1 mark*
   b The driving force is greater than the resistive force.   *1 mark*

Examiner's tip

Whether an object speeds up, slows down or maintains a steady speed depends on the balance of the forces acting. If the forces acting on an object are balanced, it stays at rest or maintains a steady speed. Unbalanced forces cause a change in speed or direction or both.

   c It decreases (slows down),   *1 mark*
        because there is no longer a driving force; because there is a net
        force against the motion.   *1 mark*

TOTAL 4 MARKS

15 a (i) Equal volumes of dilute hydrochloric acid.   *1 mark*
   (ii) Same concentration of hydrochloric acid.   *1 mark*

Examiner's tip

You should be familiar with fair testing from KS2. It means keeping everything the same except for the one thing you are varying. In this case this is the brand of indigestion tablet.

   b The solution contains the same amount of hydrochloric acid so the more antacid in
        the tablet, the fewer tablets will be needed to neutralise the acid.   *2 marks*

Examiner's tip

The examiner would award 1 mark for an answer without explanation, e.g. the one where most tablets are used up.

c Advantage: the reaction would be faster.   *1 mark*
Disadvantage: it would be more difficult to see when the powder has reacted, *or*
some of the powder might be spilled.   *1 mark*

TOTAL 6 MARKS

16 a **D**   *1 mark*
b A book scatters light or reflects it in all directions, whereas there is
regular reflection from the flat mirror.   *1 mark*
c **E**   *1 mark*

Examiner's tip
The image in a mirror is always the same distance directly behind the mirror as the object is in front of the mirror.

d They are both upright.   *1 mark*
They are the same size.   *1 mark*

TOTAL 5 MARKS

Examiner's tip
In **d**, shape and colour are also similarities but they are not the best responses to the question asked.

17 a It vibrates or oscillates/moves back and forth.   *1 mark*

Examiner's tip
All sounds are caused by the vibration of an object; in musical instruments it is usually either a string or an air column that vibrates.

b The cone moves further.   *1 mark*

Examiner's tip
The amplitude of a vibration is the greatest displacement from the rest position.

c It sounds louder.   *1 mark*

TOTAL 3 MARKS

18 a The arrow should point from the satellite towards the centre of the Earth.   *1 mark*

Examiner's tip
The force that keeps the satellite in orbit is a gravitational force. It is the Earth's pull on the satellite.

b *Any two from*:
navigation
monitoring the weather
surveillance
communications
astronomy   *1 mark each: 2 marks*

TOTAL 3 MARKS

19 a

Organ	Job of the organ
Anus	absorbs dissolved food into the blood
Oesophagus	chews the food into small pieces
Large intestine	digests protein
Mouth	passes the food to the stomach
Small intestine	excretes waste
Stomach	absorbs water from the waste

1 mark for each correct link.   *5 marks*

 **Examiner's tip**   It is important that you know the main steps in the process of digestion. Pupils often confuse the jobs of the two intestines. The food, in the form of a liquid, passes from the stomach into the small intestine. Here soluble substances pass into the blood. It then passes into the large intestine which absorbs water, leaving the solid waste which is egested through the anus.

b   Enzyme.   *1 mark*

 **Examiner's tip**   You would not be penalised if you gave a correct name for the correct enzyme, amylase.

c   Sugar molecules are much smaller than starch molecules.   *1 mark*
They can pass through the walls of the small intestine.   *1 mark*

TOTAL 8 MARKS

20 a (i)   At night water freezes   *1 mark*
and expands   *1 mark*
causing large forces which break up the rock.   *1 mark*
   (ii)   Weathering or freeze/thaw   *1 mark*
   b   Expansion when rocks are heated and contraction when cooled *1 mark*
causes stresses which break up rocks.   *1 mark*
Wind blows sand.   *1 mark*
Moving sand wears away rock.   *1 mark*

 **Examiner's tip**   This question is designed to emphasise the differences between weathering and erosion. Erosion is the wearing away of rocks by moving water, ice, sand, etc.

TOTAL 8 MARKS

21 a Here are the completed diagrams.

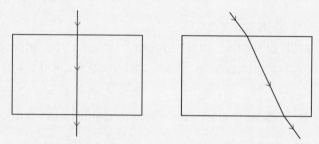

Award 1 mark for showing the light continuing in the same direction in the left-hand diagram.   *1 mark*

Award 1 mark for each correct change of direction shown in the right-hand diagram. The ray needs to be parallel to the initial ray on exit from the glass.   *2 marks*

Examiner's tip

The change in direction when light crosses a boundary is often described with reference to the normal line. This is a line drawn at right angles to the boundary. Light that travels along the normal line does not change direction.

For light that meets the boundary in any other direction, the change of direction is towards the normal line as it passes into glass or plastic and away from the normal line as it passes back into air.

b Refraction   *1 mark*
c (i) It separates into colours.   *1 mark*
  (ii) It shows that white light is a mixture of different colours.   *1 mark*

Examiner's tip

Rainbows are caused by the dispersion of white light passing through water droplets.

TOTAL 6 MARKS

22 a The Moon is seen by the light that it reflects   *1 mark*
from the Sun.   *1 mark*

Examiner's tip

Stars are so hot they give out their own light. Planets and moons are much cooler. They can only be seen by light that is reflected off them.

b (i) The largest star   *1 mark*
  (ii) The Earth's rotation on its axis makes the other stars appear to move.   *1 mark*

Examiner's tip

The largest star appears not to move because it is straight above the axis of rotation.

  (iii) 21 hours   *1 mark*

Examiner's tip

An answer of '20 hours 59 minutes' shows a very good understanding of why the stars appear to rotate. They seem to go round once each day because of the Earth's rotation on its axis, and an additional once each year because of the Earth's movement around the Sun.

TOTAL 5 MARKS

TEST TOTAL 120 MARKS

Determining your level

FINDING YOUR LEVEL IN TESTS A AND B

When you have marked a test, enter the total number of marks you scored for each question on the Marking grid opposite. Then add them up and enter the test total on the grid.

Using the total for each test, look at the charts below to determine your level for each test.

Test A

Level 3 or below	Level 4	Level 5	Level 6	Level 7	Gifted & Talent
up to 15	16–38	39–64	65–85	86–100	101+

Test B

Level 3 or below	Level 4	Level 5	Level 6	Level 7	Gifted & Talent
up to 15	16–38	39–64	65–85	86–100	101+

FINDING YOUR OVERALL LEVEL IN SCIENCE

After you have worked out separate levels for Tests A and B, add up your total marks for the two tests. Use this total and the chart below to determine your overall level in Science. The chart also shows you how your level in these tests compares with the target level for your age group.

Total for Tests A and B

Level 3 or below	Level 4	Level 5	Level 6	Level 7	Gifted & T
up to 30	31–76	77–128	129–170	171–200	201
Working towards target level for age group		Working at target level for age group		Working beyond target level	

FINDING OUT WHETHER YOU ARE STRONGER IN ONE AT

In the tables on page 75, the questions are divided into AT2 (Biology), AT3 (Chemistry) and AT4 (Physics). There are 40 marks for each AT in Test A, and in Test B there are 40 marks for AT2, 35 marks for AT3, and 45 marks for AT4.

Add up your score for each AT. These totals may help you to decide what to concentrate on in your revision.

Marking grid

Test A Pages 12–32

Question	AT	Marks available	Marks scored	Question	AT	Marks available	Marks scored
1	4	5		11	4	4	
2	2	7		12	4	6	
3	2	7		13	3	8	
4	4	4		14	4	3	
5	4	6		15	4	4	
6	3	7		16	2	8	
7	2	7		17	3	8	
8	3	8		18	4	3	
9	2	11		19	4	5	
10	3	9		Total		120	

Test B Pages 33–56

Question	AT	Marks available	Marks scored	Question	AT	Marks available	Marks scored
1	4	3		13	2	9	
2	3	7		14	4	4	
3	2	4		15	3	6	
4	2	5		16	4	5	
5	4	5		17	4	3	
6	3	6		18	4	3	
7	2	5		19	2	8	
8	4	5		20	3	8	
9	4	6		21	4	6	
10	2	4		22	4	5	
11	2	5		Total		120	
12	3	8					

First published in 1997
New Edition 2003

Test: © Letts Educational Ltd 2003-06-24
Authors: Lynn Huggins-Cooper (English); Mark Patmore and Brian Seager(Maths); Bob McDuell and Graham Booth (Science)

Series Editor: Bob Mc Duell

Design and illustrations:
© Letts Educational 2003

All our Rights Reserved. No part of this publication may be reproduced, stored in a retrieval system or transmitted, in any form or by any means, electronic, mechanical, photocopying, recording or otherwise, without the prior permission of Letts Educational.

British Library Cataloguing in Publication Data

A CIP record for this book is available from the British Library.

ISBN 1843153491

Cover design by 2idesign, Cambridge
Cover logo by Starfish Design for Print, London
Project management and typesetting by Cambridge Publishing Management Ltd and Hardlines Ltd

Printed in Italy

Letts Educational Ltd
The Chiswick Centre
414 Chiswick High Road
London W4 5TF
Telephone: 020 8996 3333
Fax: 020 8742 8390
e-mail: mail@lettsed.co.uk
website: www.letts-education.com

Letts Educational Limited is a division of Granada Learning Limited, part of Granada plc.

National Curriculum
Key Stage 3 Age 13–14

National Test Practice Papers

Practice English
Practice Maths
Practice Science

3 in 1 Contents